D0215499

Biography
Ann Patrick Green

Ann Patrick Green is a graduate of the Eastman School of Music (University of Rochester, N.Y.) where she received both a Bachelor of Music with Distinction and a Master of Music degree in Piano Performance. She later studied at the University of Colorado towards a Doctor of Musical Arts degree in Piano Performance and Pedagogy. Her teachers included Cecile Genhart, Frank Mannheimer, Beryl Rubinstein, Arthur Loesser.

She began her teaching career in 1957 at Eastman and has served as faculty at the University of Colorado, Maryville College, Tennessee, Fullerton College, and California State University, Fullerton. She has also been a guest lecturer at Fullerton College and California State University, Fullerton.

She is a member of the Music Teachers National Association, Music Teachers Association of California, Musical Arts Club, Sigma Alpha Iota, and American College of Musicians. She serves as a judge for Piano Guild and Certificate of Merit.

Ann is Principal and Chairperson of the teaching faculty at Patrick's Music School in Fullerton. She appears often as concert pianist and chamber music player and coordinates the Richard Nixon Library and Birthplace (Yorba Linda, California) Family Concert Series.

Dedication and Acknowledgement

These "Piano Music for Little Fingers" books are dedicated to my children Heather Patrick Orozco (cover design and theory pages), Laura Patrick, and Hershel Green (patience, support, and love).

ANN PATRICK GREEN

Contents

Preface to the Teacher

This book continues on in a logical fashion from Book 1

1. New more complicated songs in the key of G including using 3/4 time are presented.

2. The key of F is introduced in the same manner as keys of C and G.

3. Extended hand position is begun with use of 6 note melodies and crossing over thumb with index finger.

4. The IV chord is introduced in all keys.

5. Dotted rhythms are introduced.

6. Dynamic indications, staccato and legato touches are utilized in pieces as well as two-note and longer phrases.

7. Transposition of previous melodies to new keys is introduced.

8. The use of Solfege as well as alphabet letters for music language is continued.

Music Facts and Note Reading

𝄞   Treble (So or G) clef - a music sign used for higher notes.

𝄢   Bass (Fa or F) clef - a music sign used for lower notes.

4/4   Time signature - means each measure contains four beats and a quarter note gets one beat.

♩   Quarter note - one beat of sound.

𝄽   Quarter rest - one beat of silence.

♫   Eighth notes - two equal one beat of sound.

♩   Half note - two beats of sound.

f   Forte means loud.

p   Piano means soft.

   Grand staff is the treble and bass clef braced together.

{   Brace - used to tie the bass and treble clefs together.

   Measure - the space between the bar lines.

   Chord - the word used to indicate two or more notes played at the same time.

mp   Mezzopiano - means medium soft.

mf   Mezzoforte - means medium loud.

♩.   Dotted half note (half note dot) - three beats and a quarter note gets one beat.

3/4   Time signature - means each measure contains three beats and a quarter note gets one beat.

𝅝   Whole note (great big whole note) - four beats of sound.

♯   Sharp sign - means to play the black key (or white key in places where there are no black keys) to the right of the named note.

   Key signature - the sharp or flat signs placed beside the clef signs. These indicate which notes are to be played sharp or flat the entire song.

sfz   Sforzando - means suddenly loud.

▬   Whole rest - one measure of silence.

▬   Half rest - two beats of silence.

D.C. al Fine   Da Capo al Fine - means to go back to the beginning and end at fine (finish).

Music Facts and Note Reading

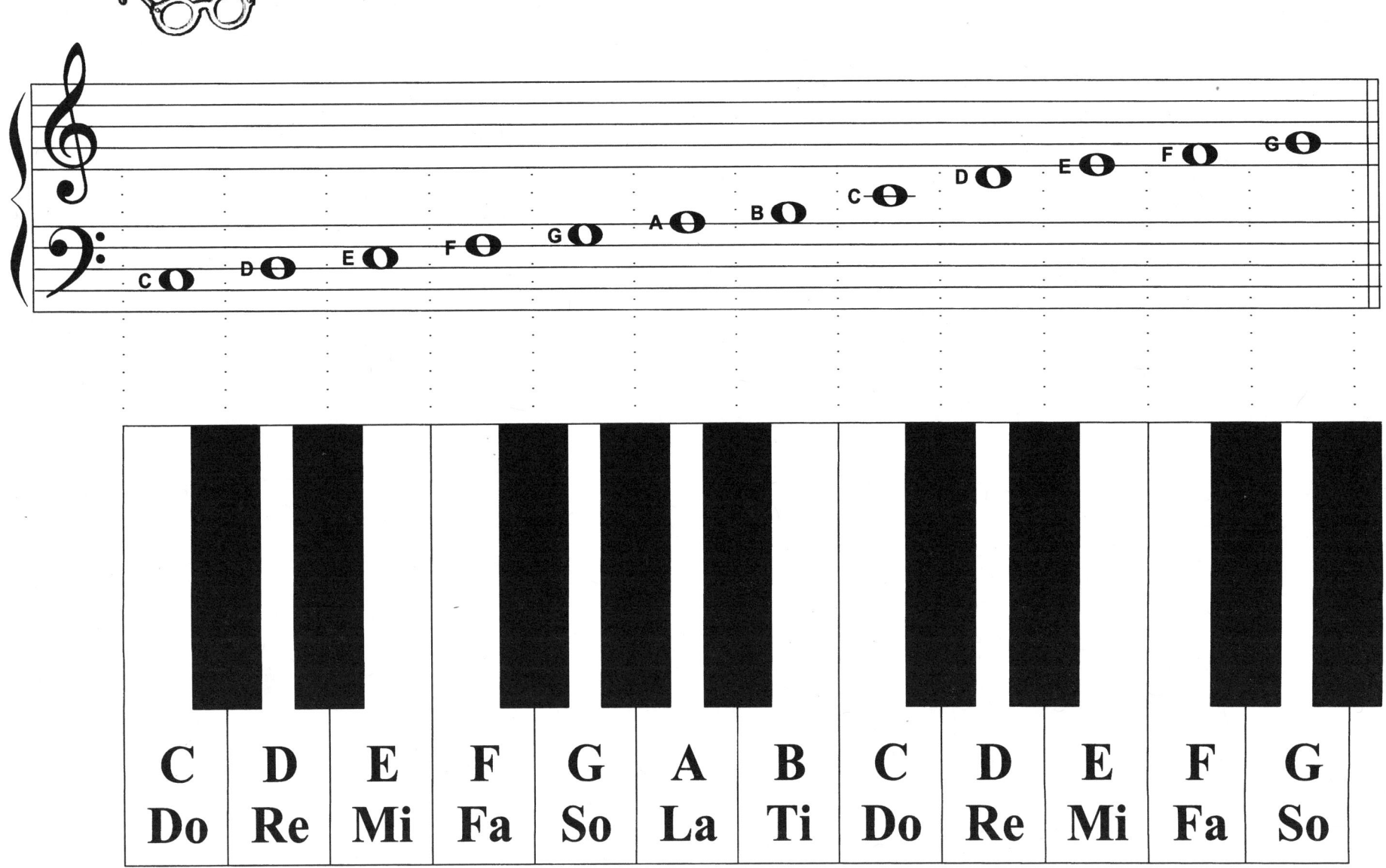

Music Facts and Note Reading

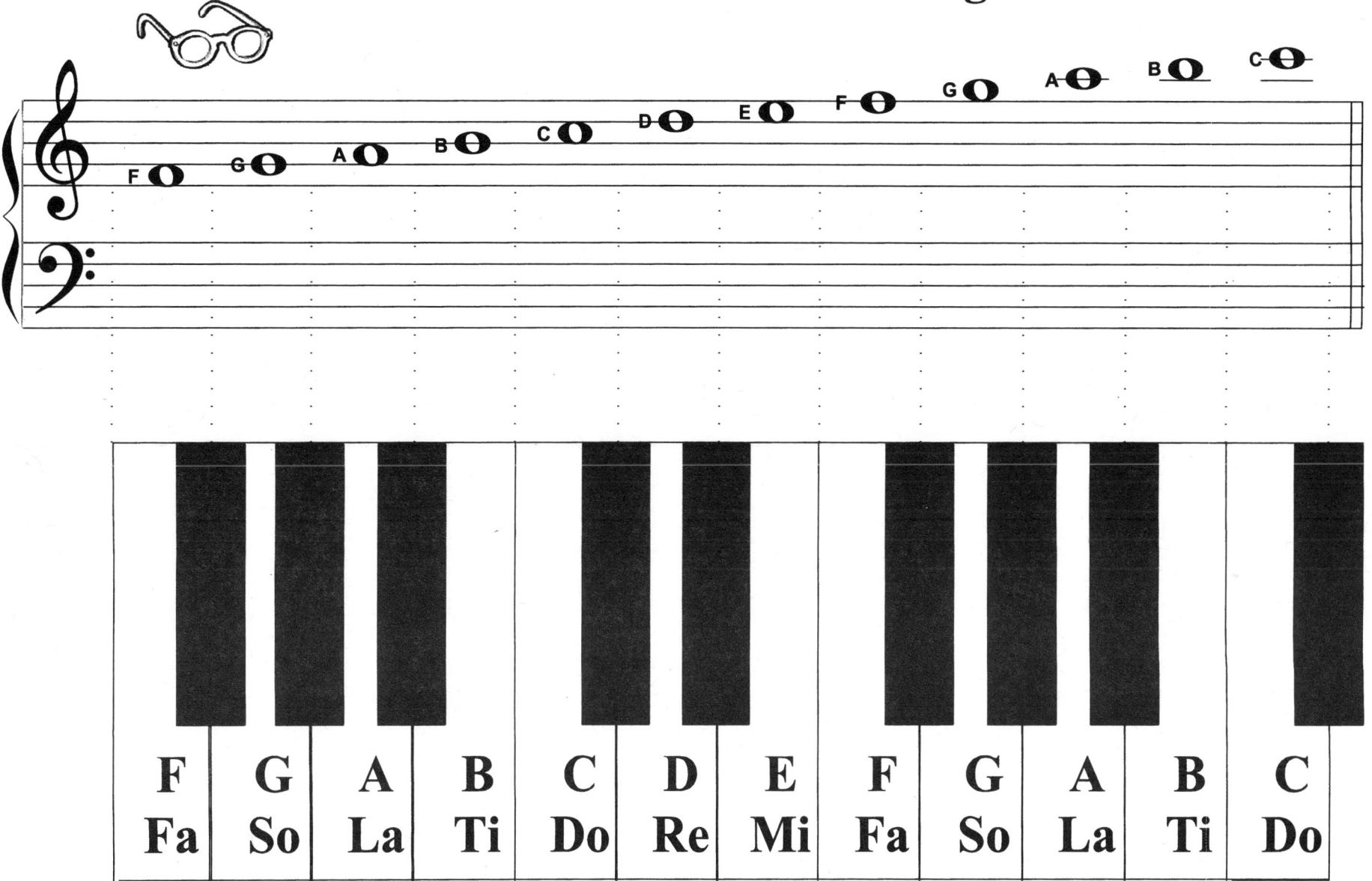

Eency Weency Spider

1. Sing song with words, then by note names.
2. Clap the rhythm.
3. Play each hand alone and sing note names.
4. Play hands together.

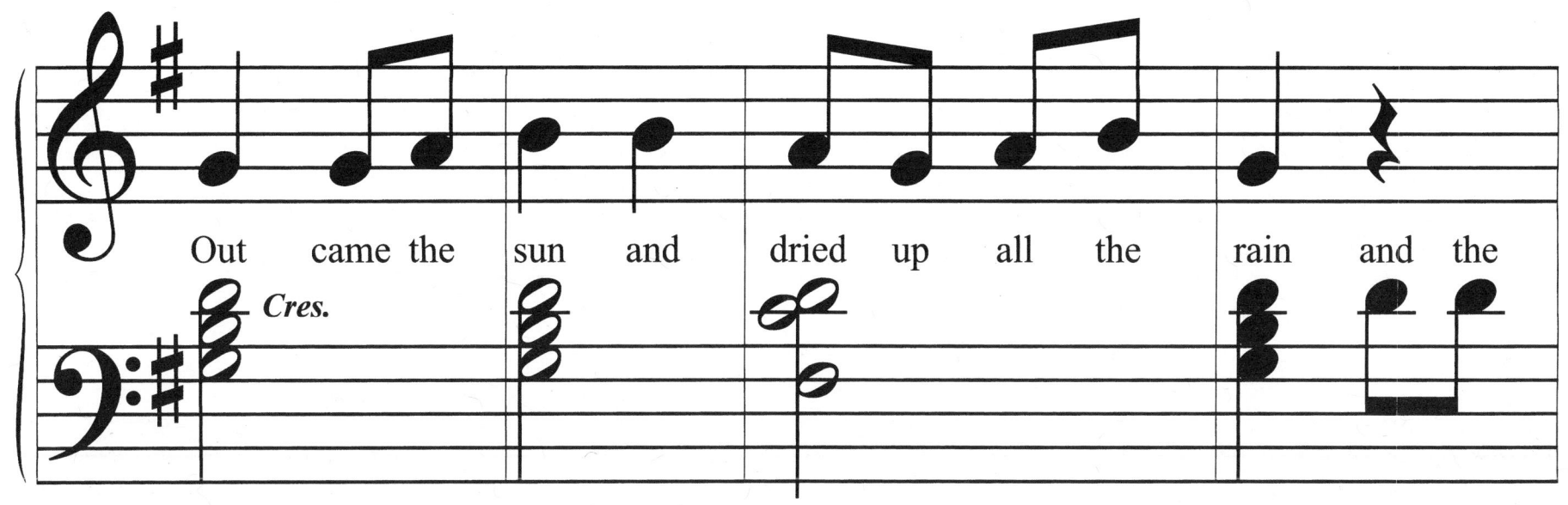

So (G) Position Do (C) Chord

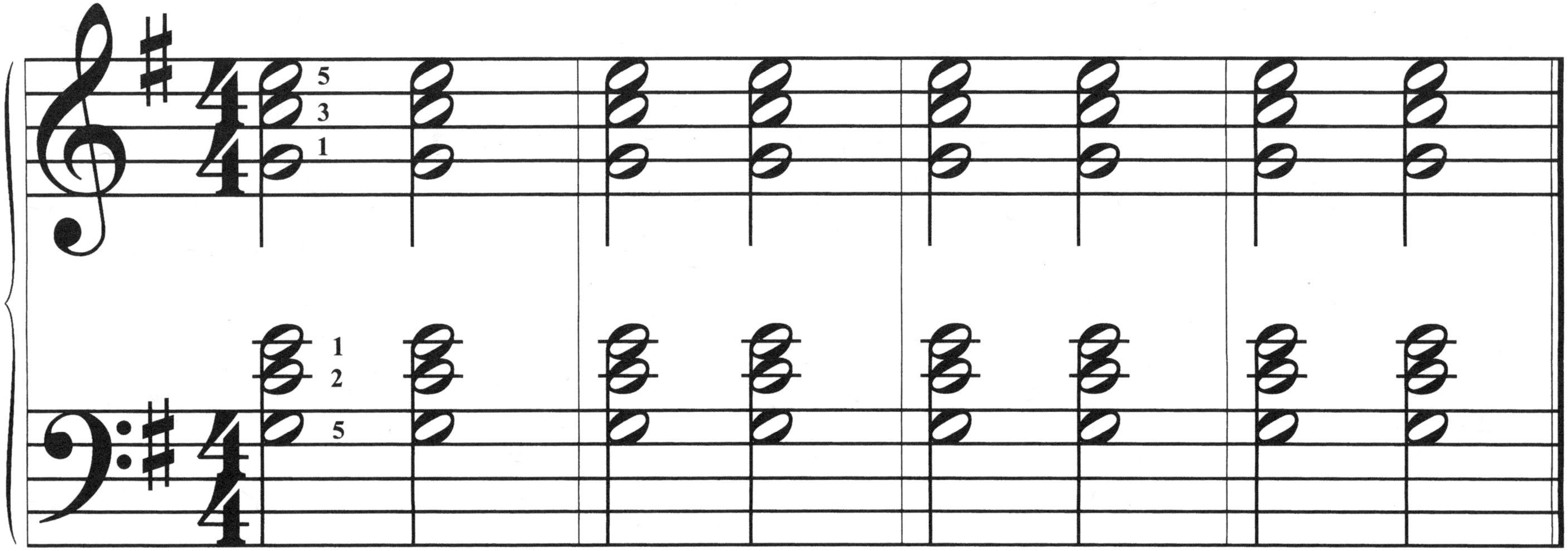

This is a new way to play the Do (C) chord.

Right Hand uses 1 (Thumb) on So (G),

3 (Tallman) on Do (C), and 5 (Pinky) on Mi (E).

Left Hand uses 5 (Pinky) on So (G), 2 (Pointer)

on Do (C), and 1 (Thumb) on Mi (E).

Three So (G) Position Chords

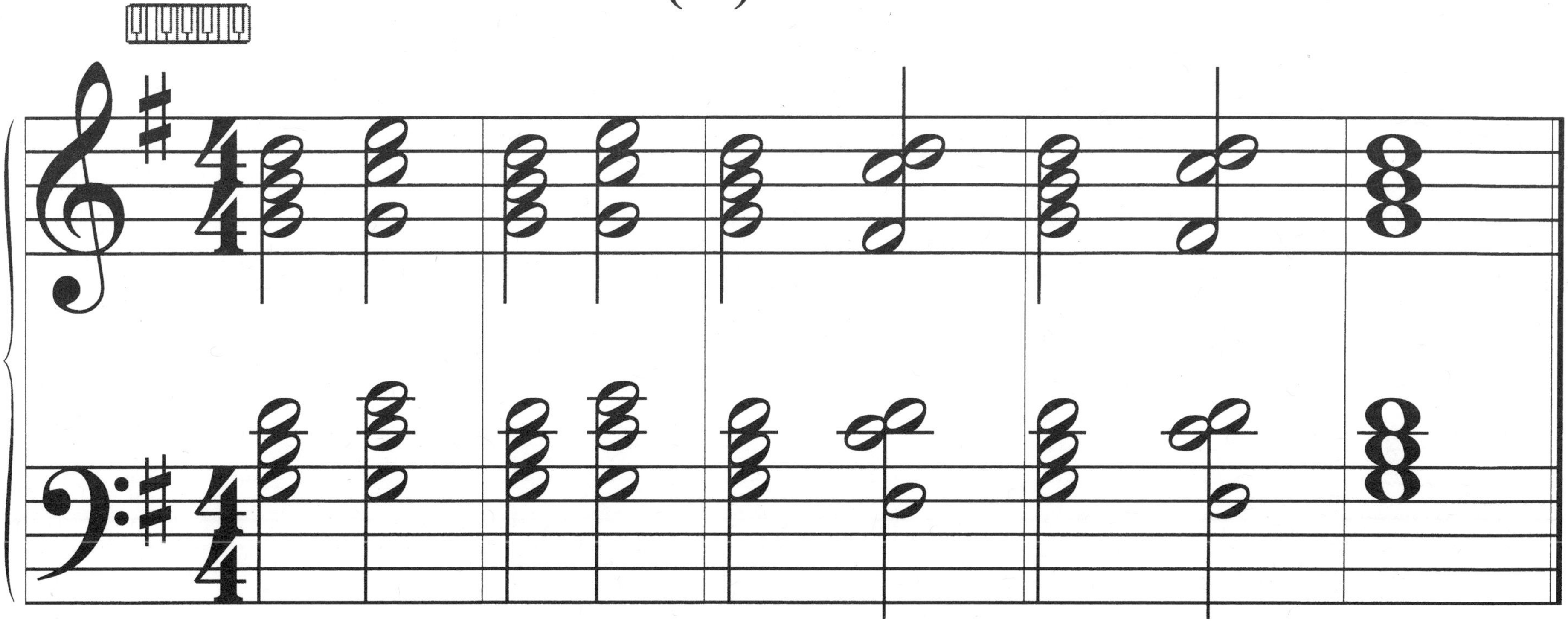

Lavender's Blue

This is a pretty folk song which may sound familiar.
Left hand uses the three So (G) position chords from page 11.
Right hand has two new signs for finger "touches". *See* next page.

Folk song

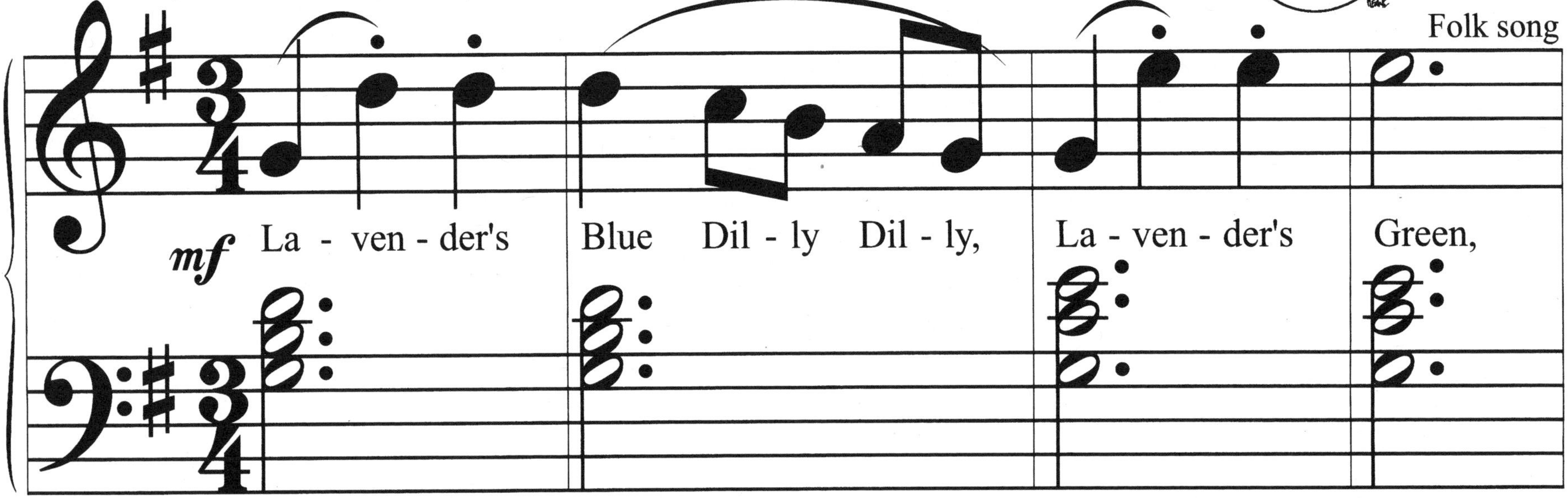

mf La - ven - der's Blue Dil - ly Dil - ly, La - ven - der's Green,

When I am King Dil - ly Dil - ly, You shall be Queen.

1. A curved line ⌒ is called a phrase line or slur. It means to play all the notes under it as a group. It's like a phrase in a story or a poem. No breathing (lifting fingers) until the end.
2. A dot on top of or below the note is called staccato. It means to let the key bounce back up as soon as you hear sound.

Who told you so Dil - ly, Dil - ly? Who told you so?

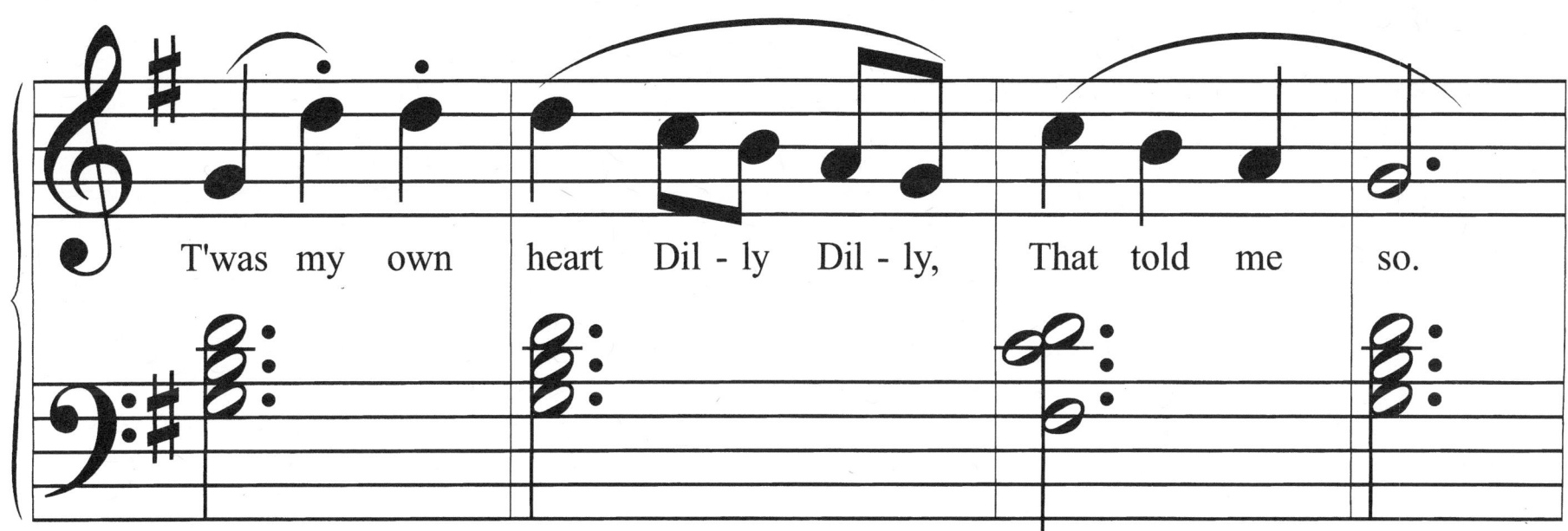

T'was my own heart Dil - ly Dil - ly, That told me so.

About Our Dog and Me

This song is also in So (G) position but, expands to six notes in the melody on page 15.
Watch the changes in fingering to help play the extra high note Mi (E).
Notice the new direction at the end of page 15 (*D.S. al Fine*). It means to go back to the
special sign at the top of the page and play to the word Fine.

Ann Patrick Green

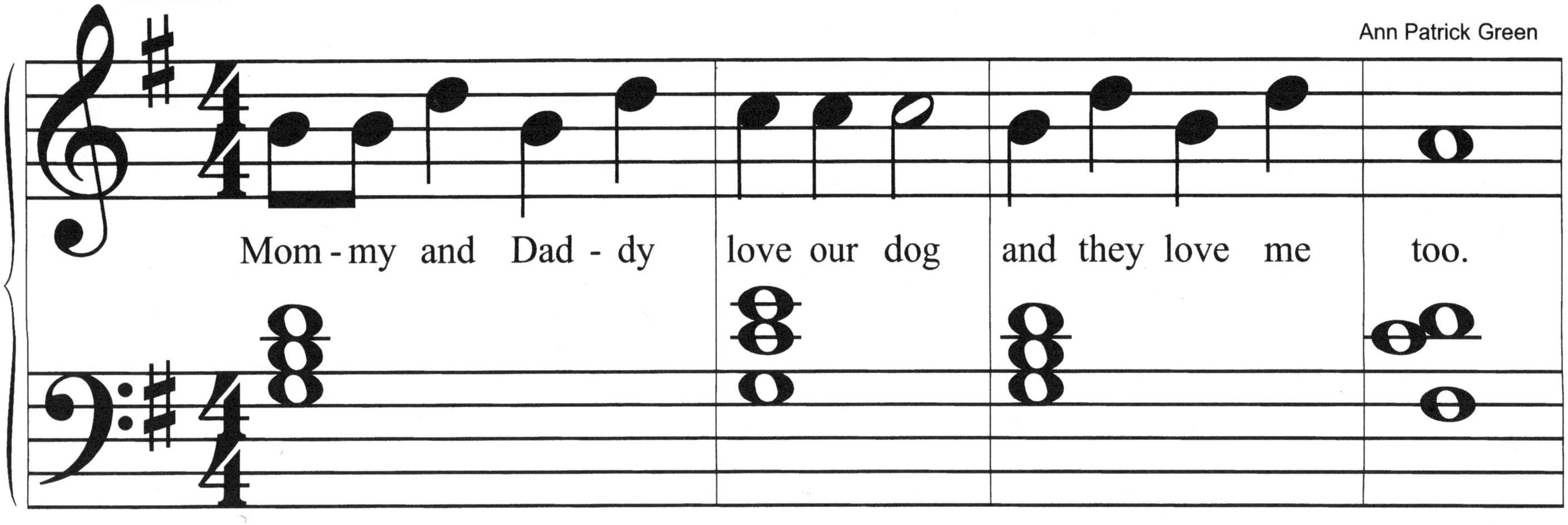

Mom-my and Dad-dy love our dog and they love me too.

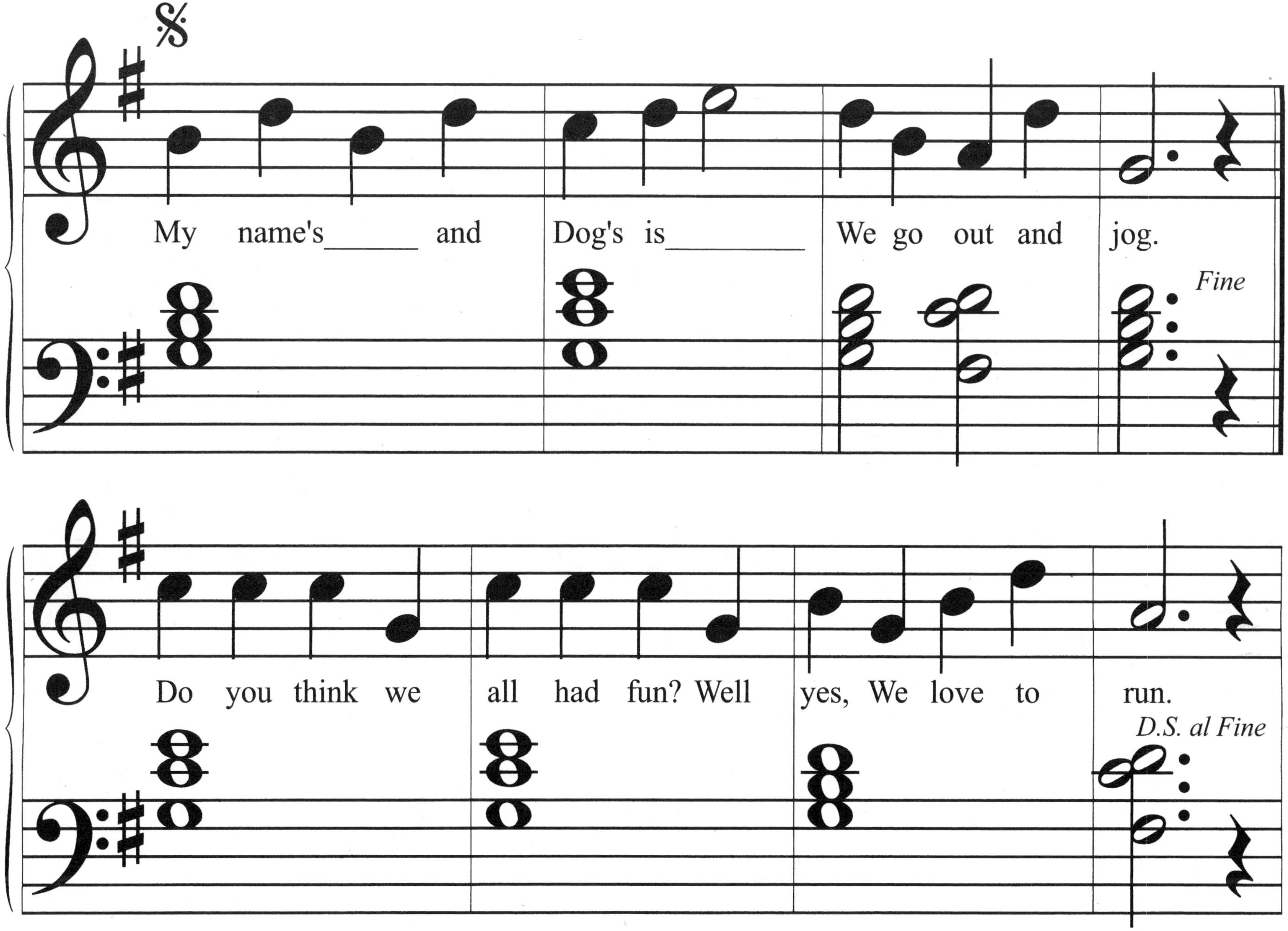

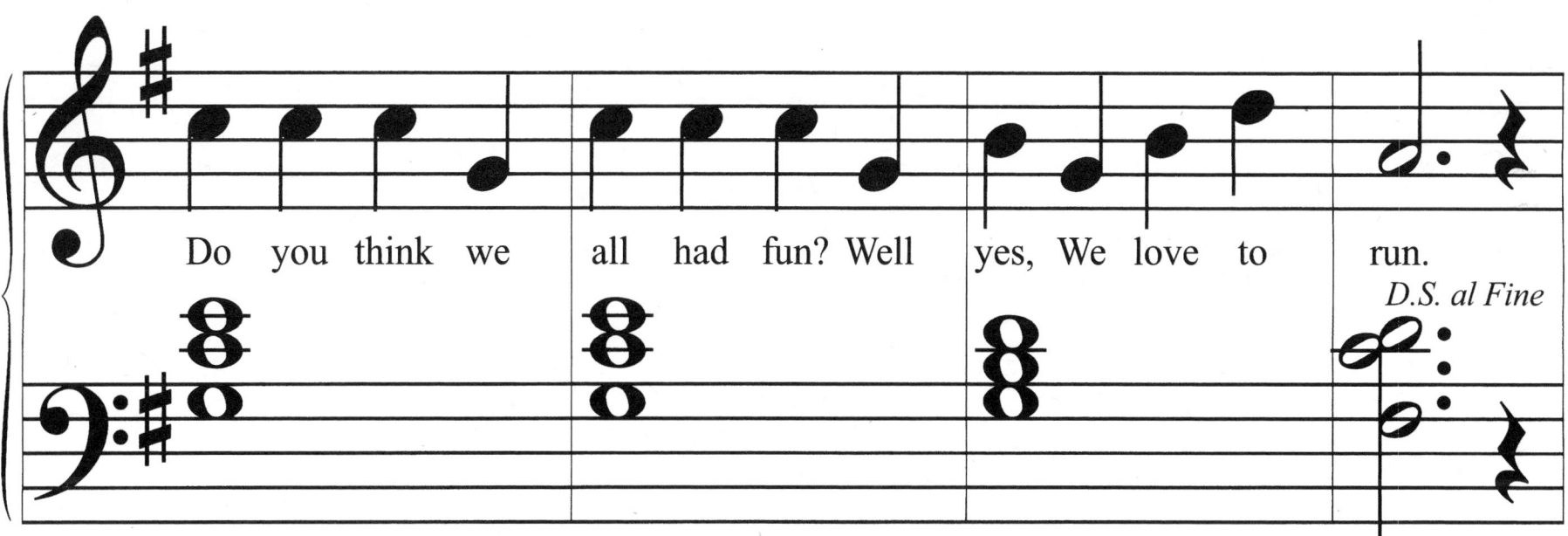

Come Out and Play

New in this song are three things:

1. Notice the single note in front of the first bar line. This is called an upbeat. Its value is then subtracted from the last measure.

2. This new note ♪ is a single 8th note. There have been two of them together before (♫).
    In this song, the dot beside the first quarter note (tahn) equals half a beat.
    The dot plus the 8th note equal one beat.

3. Two dots at the end of the first line mean to repeat the first line.

Dotted quarter   8th note

German Folk Song

Repeat sign

1. Please come and play with me to - day. We'll have a - lot of fun.
2. I have some toys. I have a bike. We'll play out in the sun.

Upbeat →

The Fly and the Bumblebee

Notice the new curved line called a "tie". It goes between notes that are the same pitch and means to hold the second note for it's full value and not play it again.

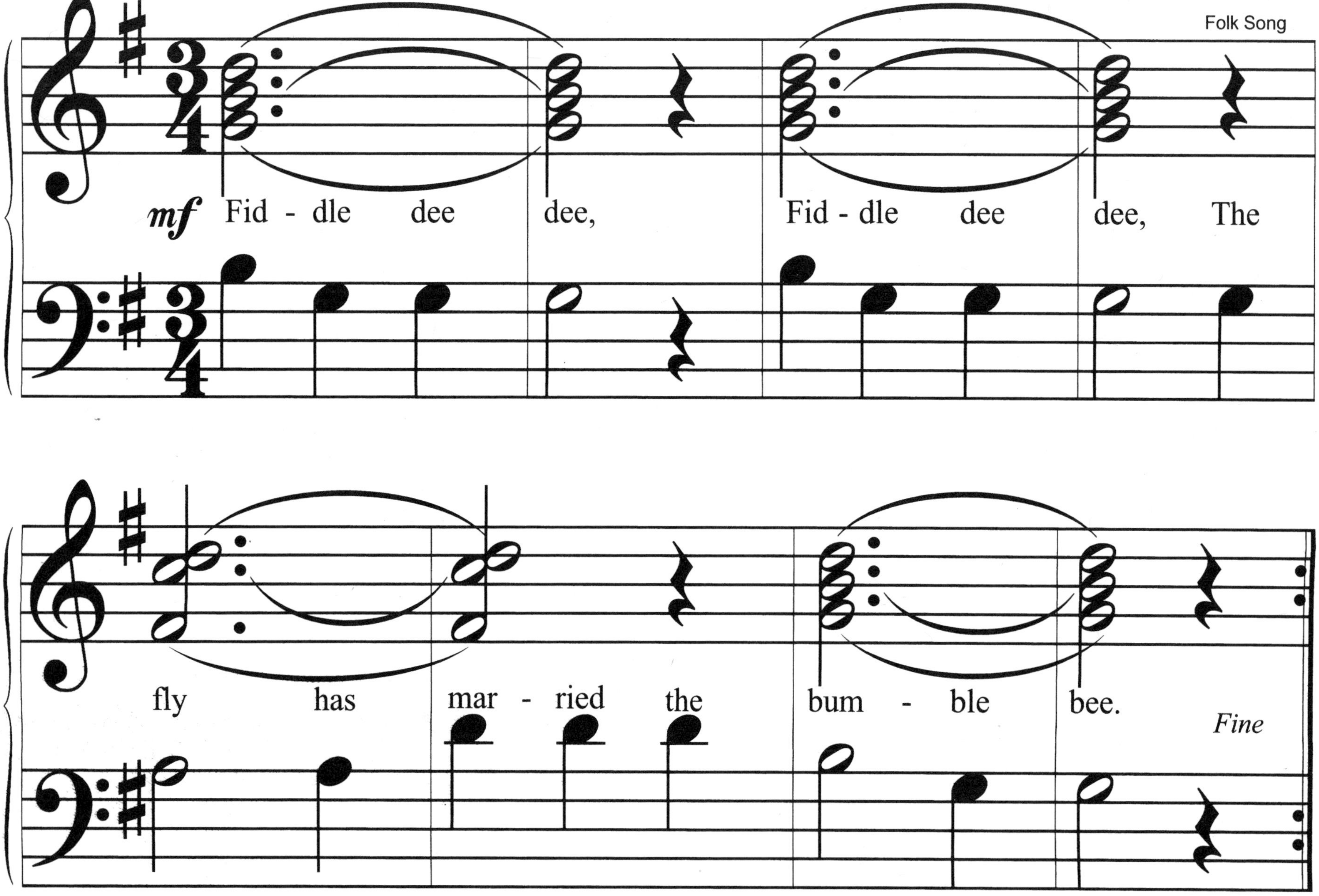

Folk Song

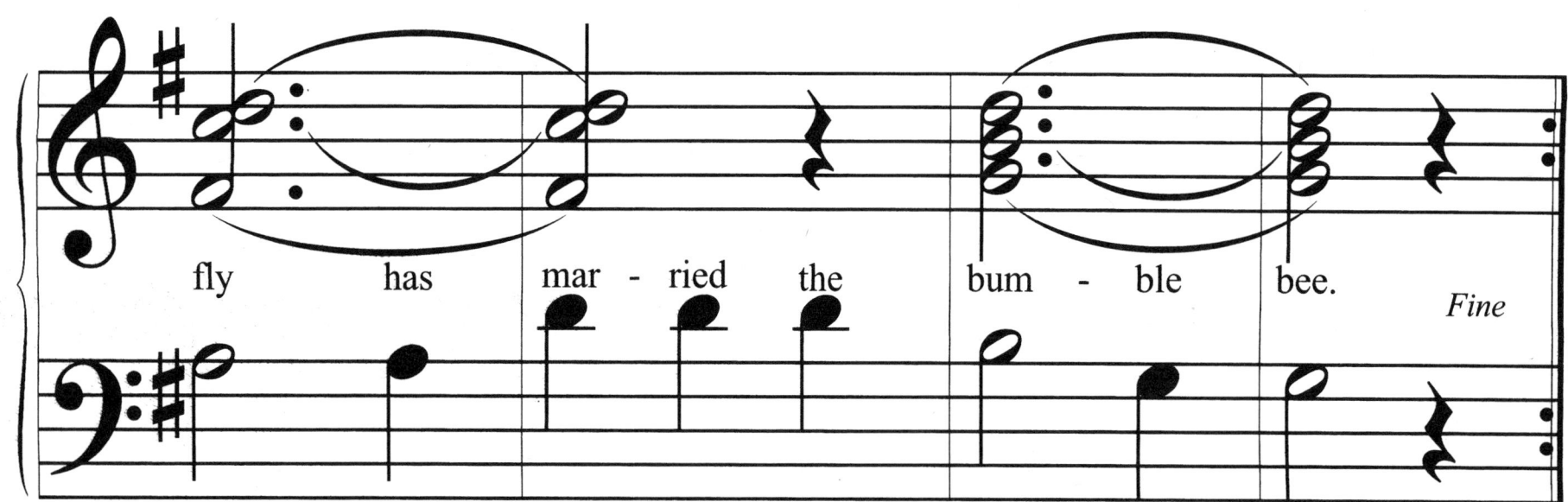

Fid - dle dee dee, Fid - dle dee dee, The fly has mar - ried the bum - ble bee.

Fine

18

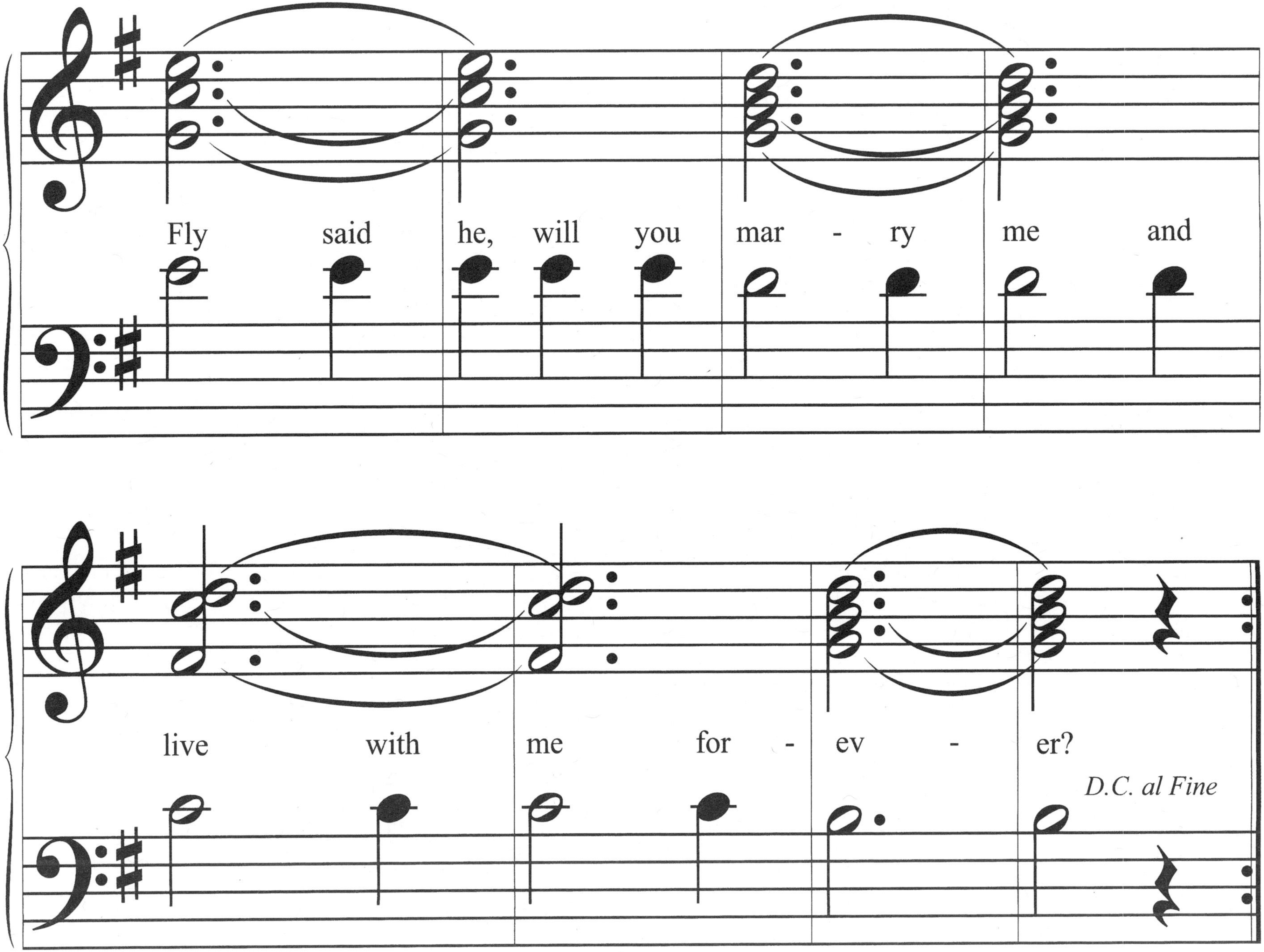

Fly said he, will you mar - ry me and live with me for - ev - er?

D.C. al Fine

Transposition Practice

Transposition means to play music in a different place on the keys.
Go back to Primer and Book I and play those songs in So (G) position.

20

Fa (F) Position Exercise

This new position has a black key called a flat. When this sign is in the music, it means to play the black key to the left of the white key. In case there is no black key, play the white key to the left. Notice the flat for Ti (B) is now part of the key signature.

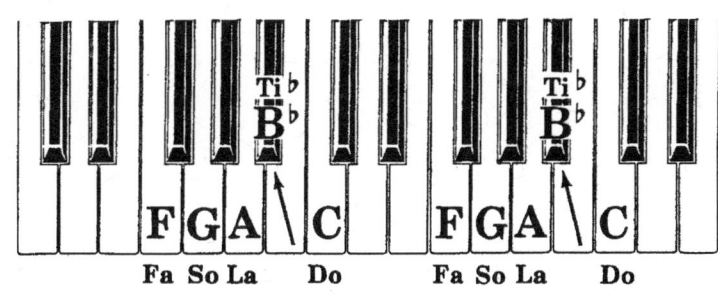

(Flat sign now in key signature. Don't forget to play Ti♭ (B♭) black key.)

Flat sign

21

Two Note Fa (F) Position Chords

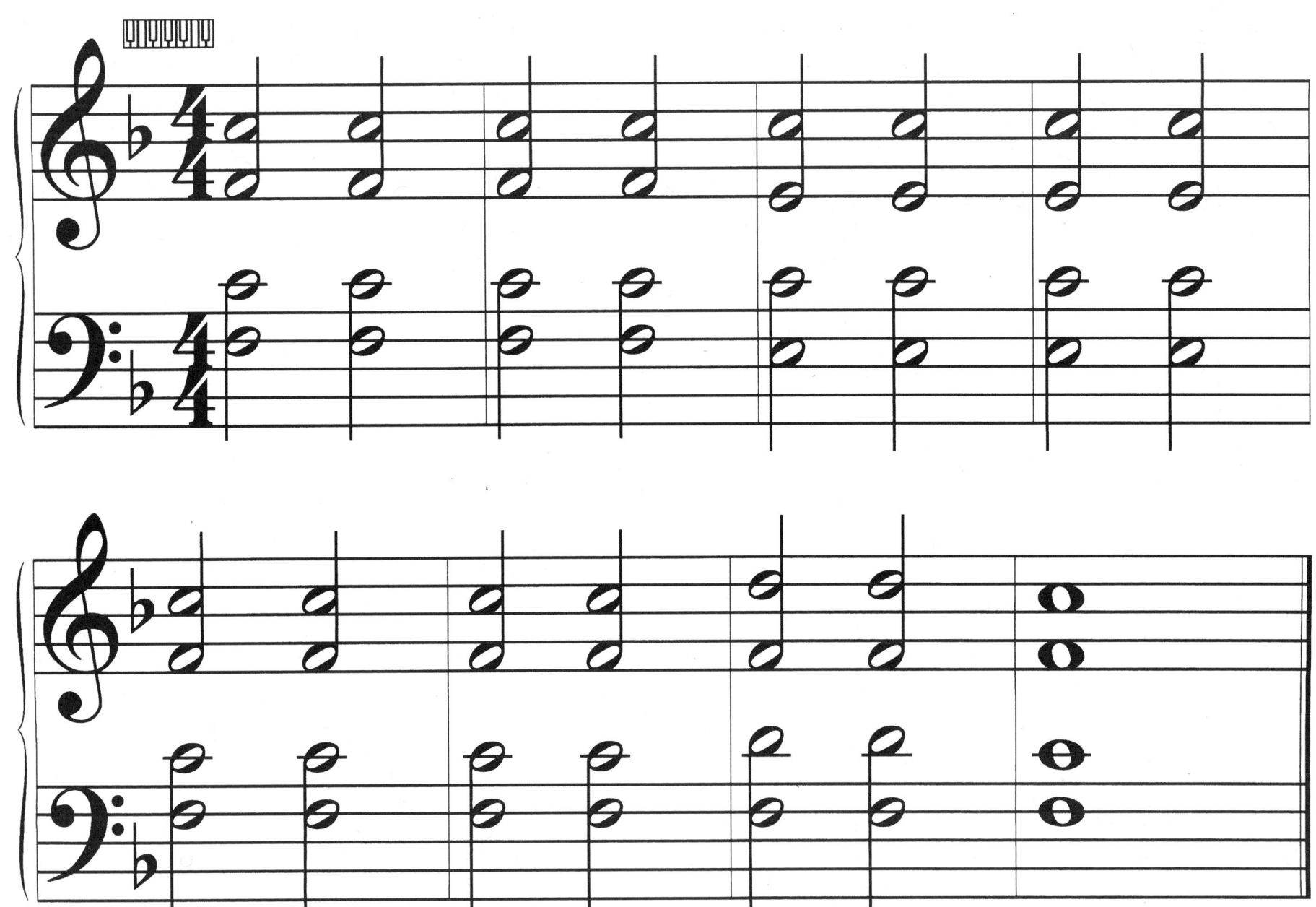

Go Tell Aunt Rhodie

Folk Song

Jeffy's Lullabye

Largo (Slow)

After learning this beautiful folk song, try playing it one octave higher.

Sleep Sleep Jef-fy, close your eyes._____ Sleep sleep Jef-fy,

don't you cry. *Fine* Snug-gle close to me, I will keep things safe for you.

24

You can dream of cake and of ice cream too; so - da cook - ies,___ all those things. You will sleep while___ I___ sing.

D.C. al Fine

La (A) Do (C), Ti♭ (B♭) Do (C), and Ti♭ (B♭) Re (D) Chords

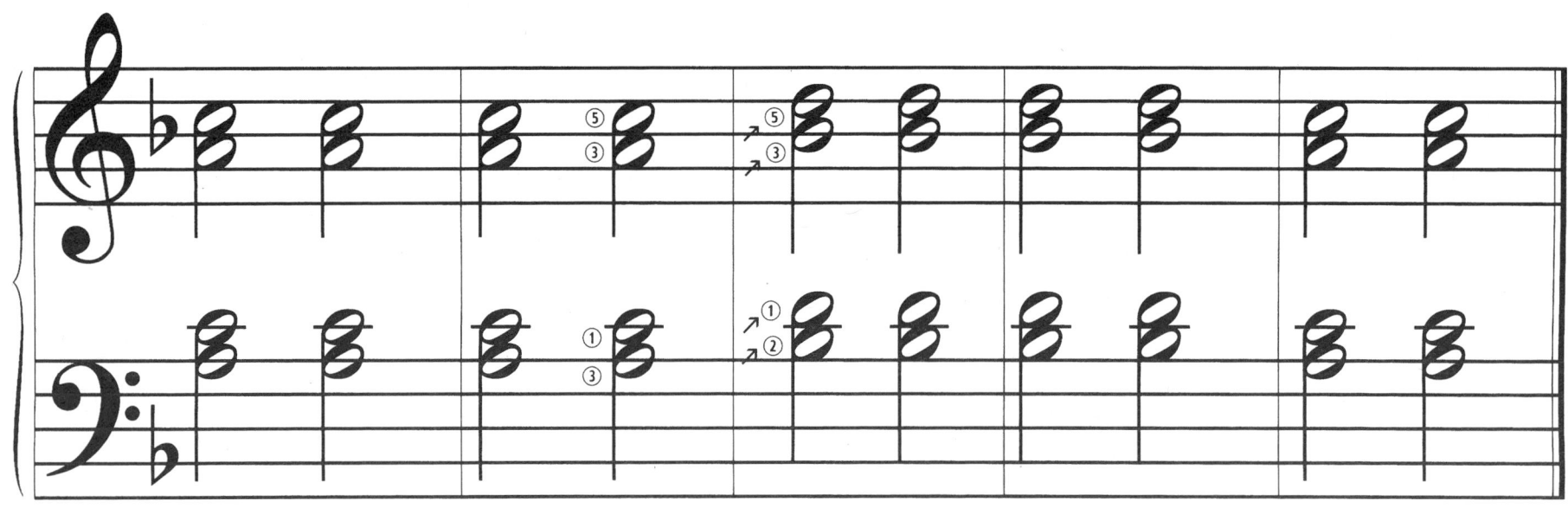

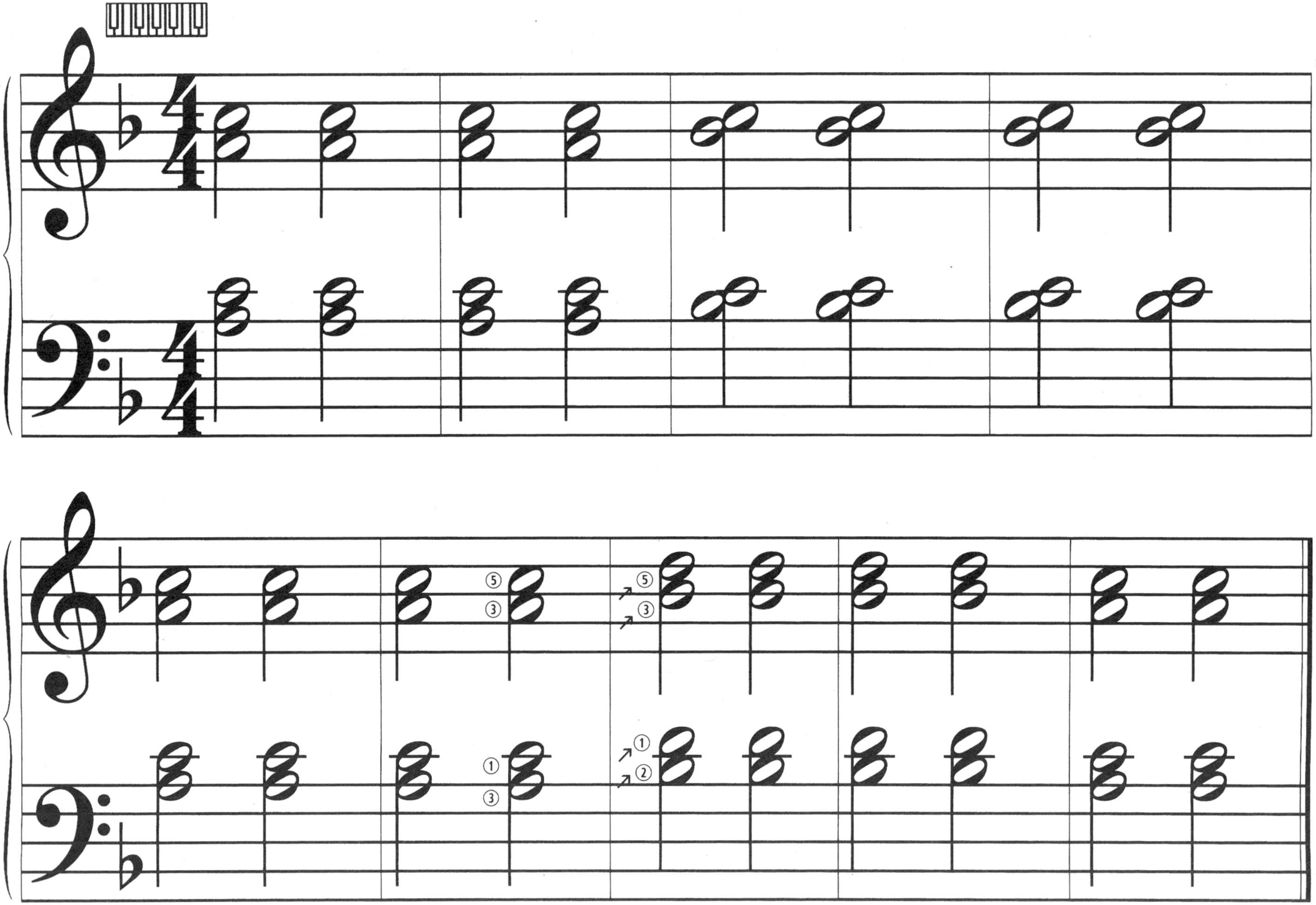

Green Gravel

Andante (Walking speed)

English Folk Song

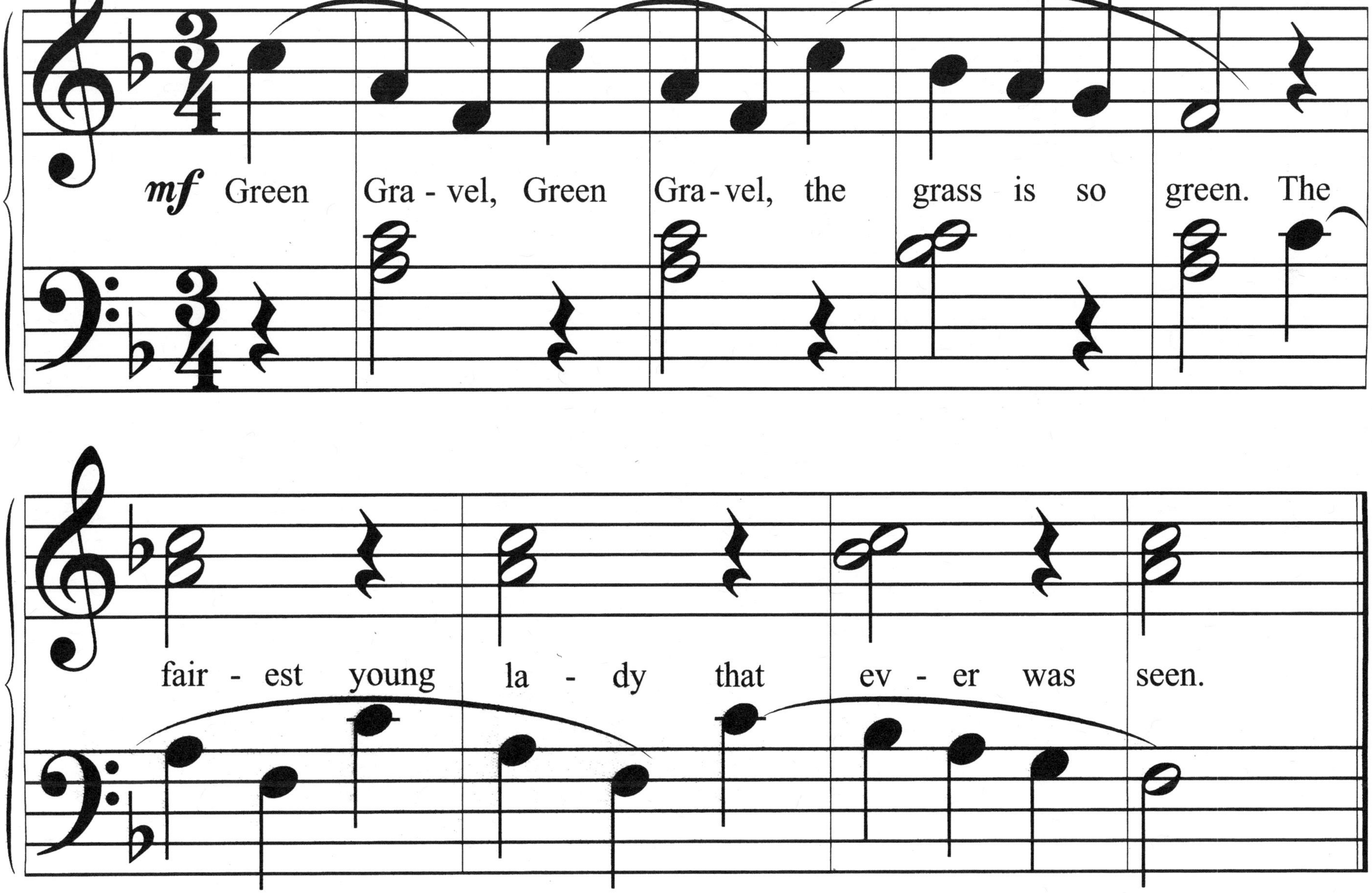

mf Green Gra - vel, Green Gra - vel, the grass is so green. The

fair - est young la - dy that ev - er was seen.

Three Note Fa (F) Position Chords

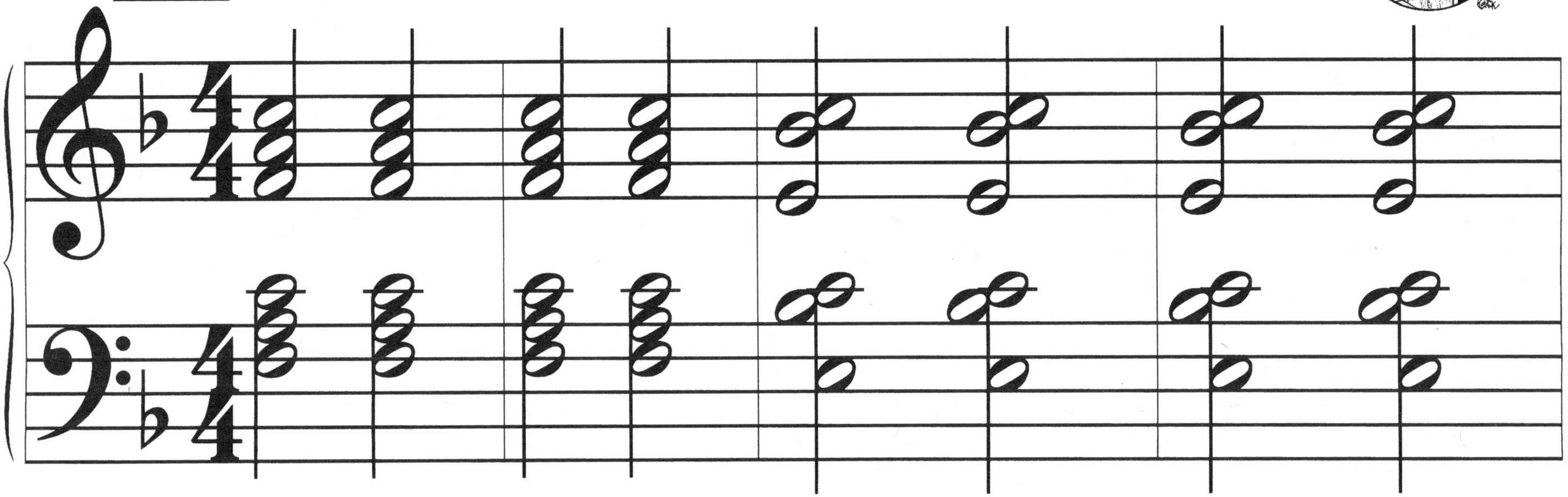

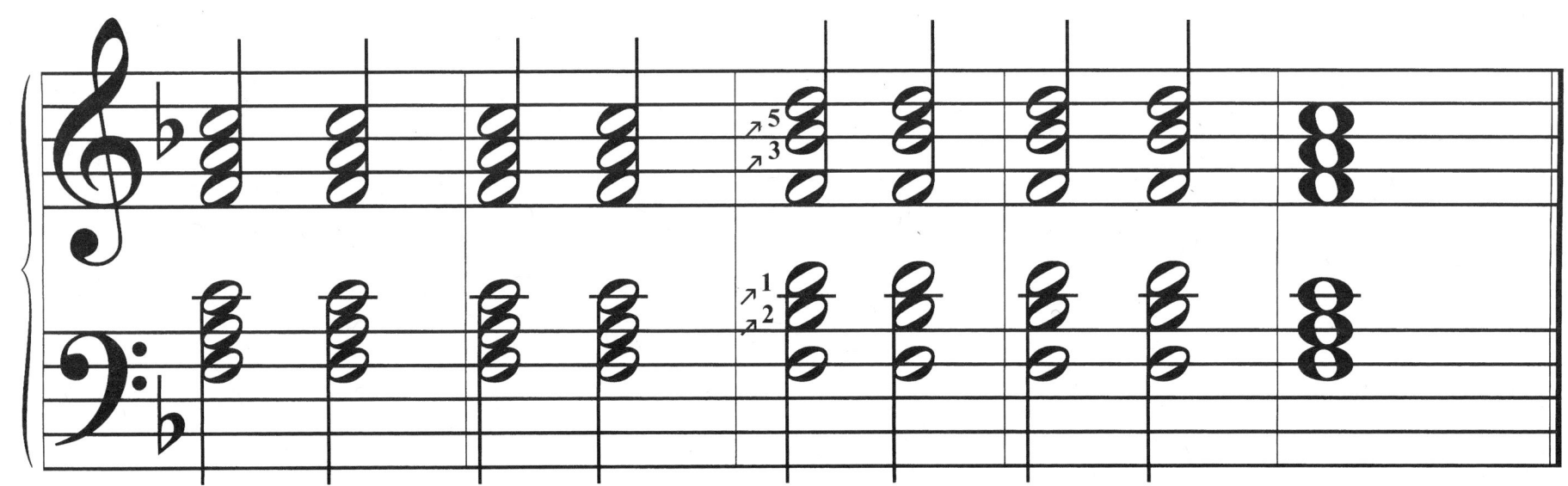

Music Symbol/Question Match

Answer the following questions

Connect answer to correct Symbol

1. What kind of note equals four counts?
(great big) _____ _____

2. What kind of rest looks like a hole in the ground?
(great big) _____ _____

3. What are 2 notes that go really fast together but only equal one beat?
_____ _____

4. What is the magic number to find Bass Clef Do?
_____

5. What kind of note do you have to hold for two counts?
_____ _____

6. Who is in charge of the high sounds?
Mrs. _____ _____

7. Who is in charge of the low sounds?
Mr. _____ _____

8. What are the note names in Do (C) position?
_____, _____, _____, _____, _____

9. What are the note names in So (G) position?
_____, _____, _____, _____, _____

The Bear Went Over the Mountain

Notice the new sign ⌢ . It is called "Fermata"
and means to hold the note longer than it's value.

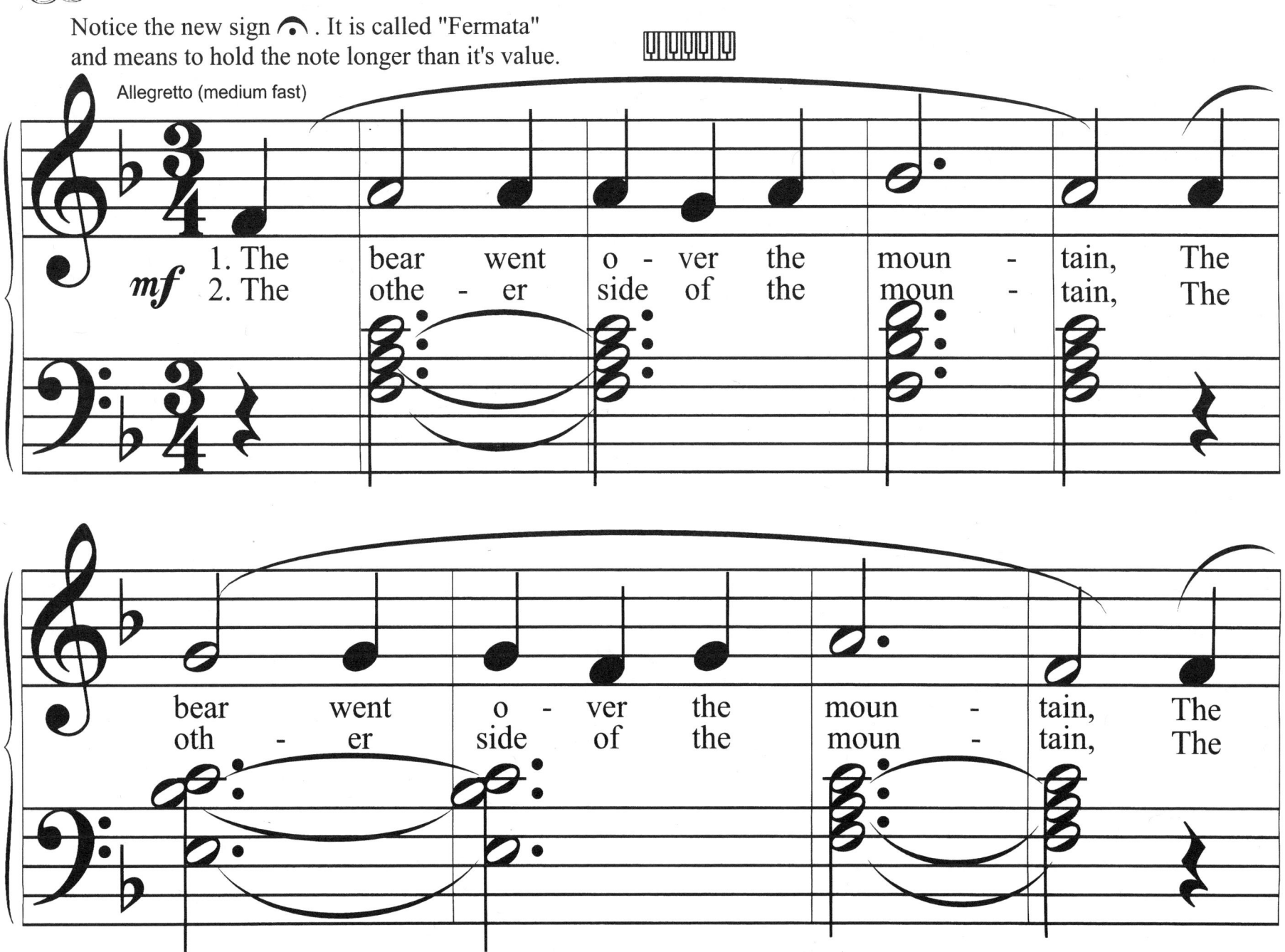

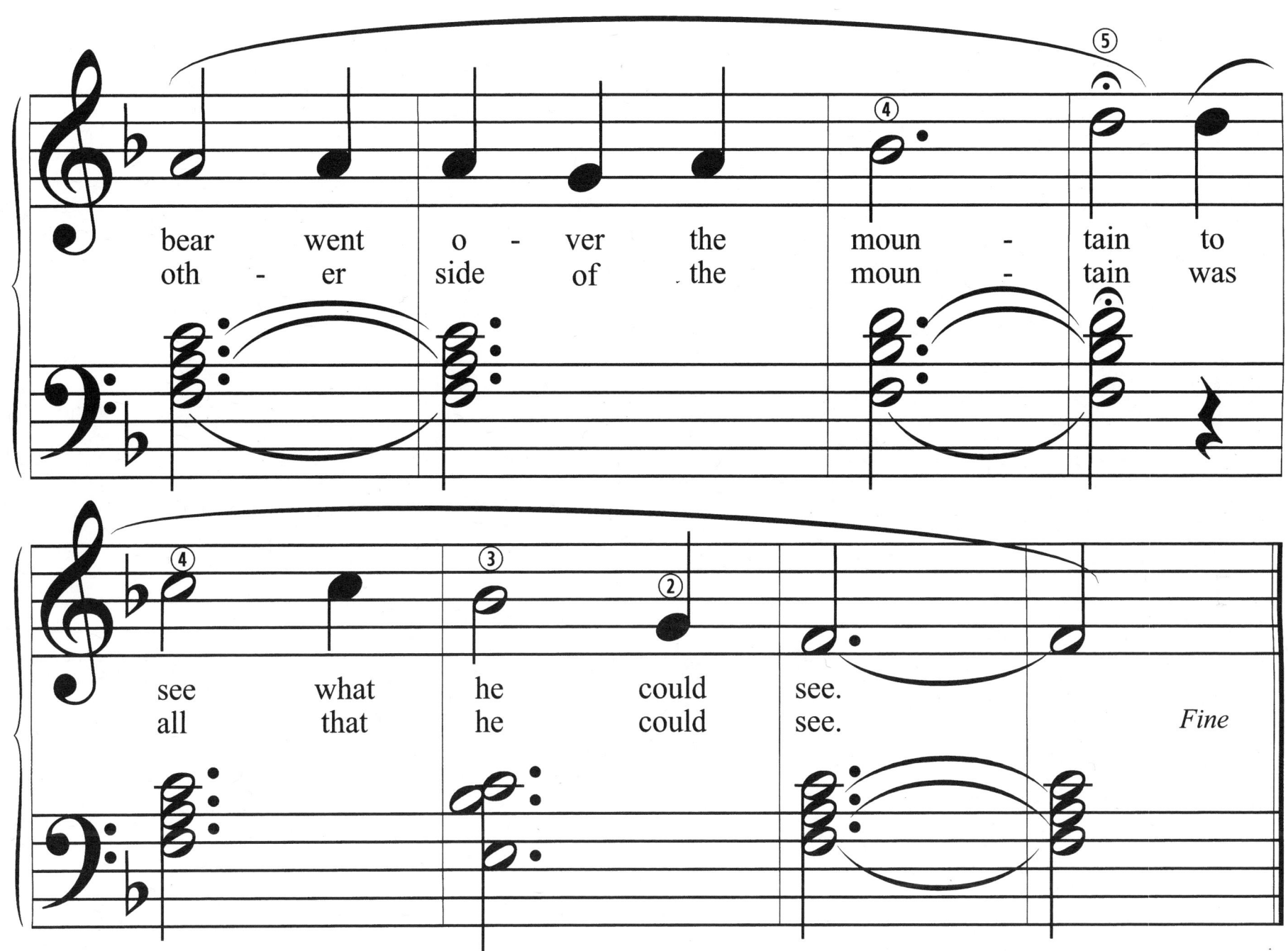

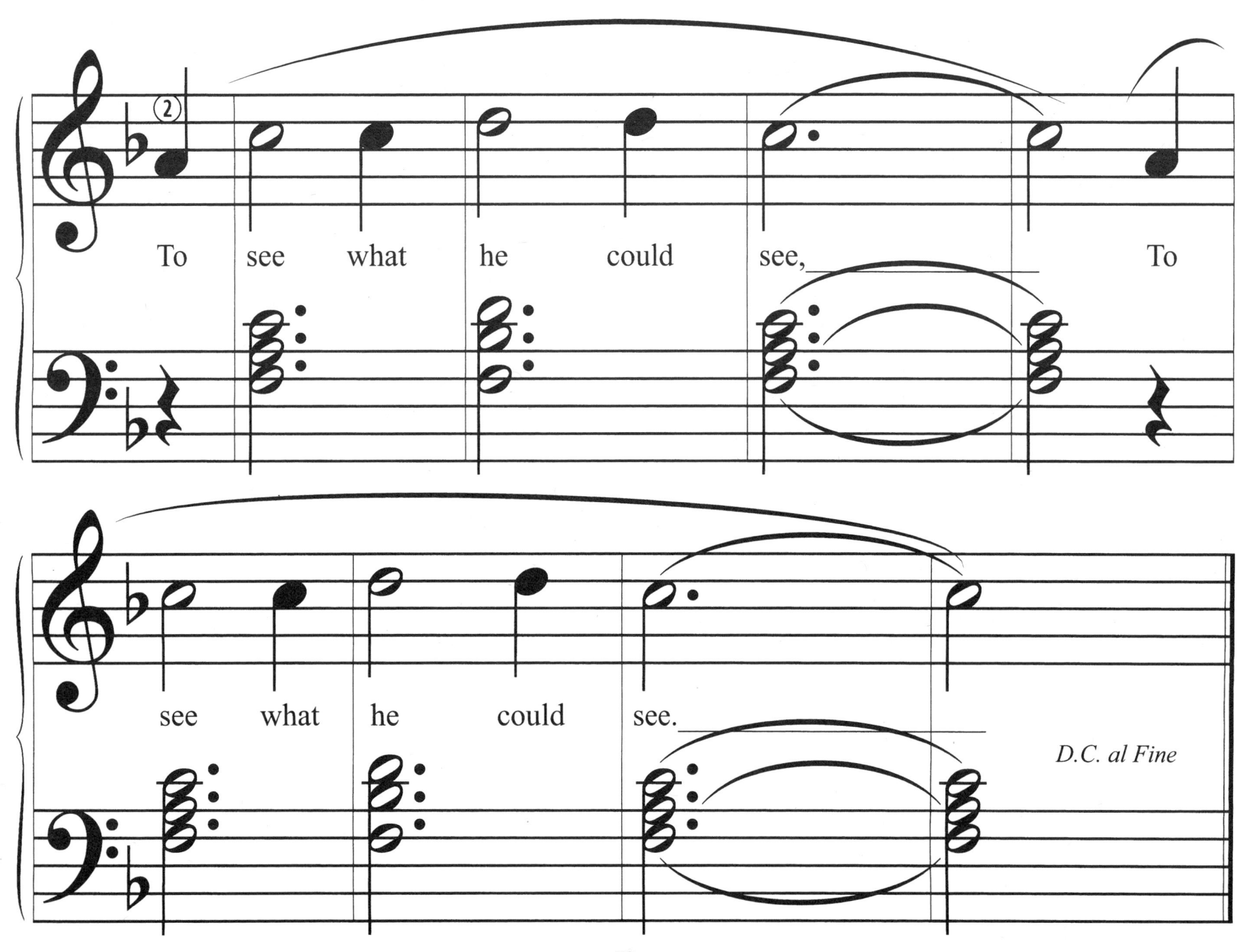

To see what he could see,_ To

see what he could see._

D.C. al Fine

Drawing Notes in Both Clefs

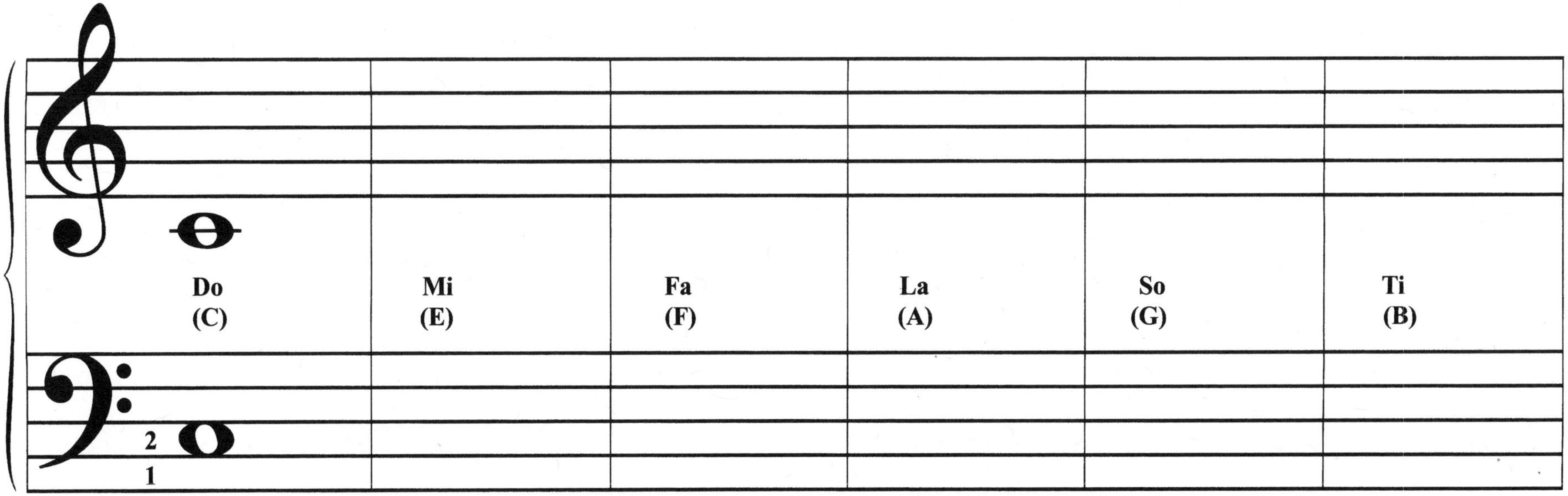

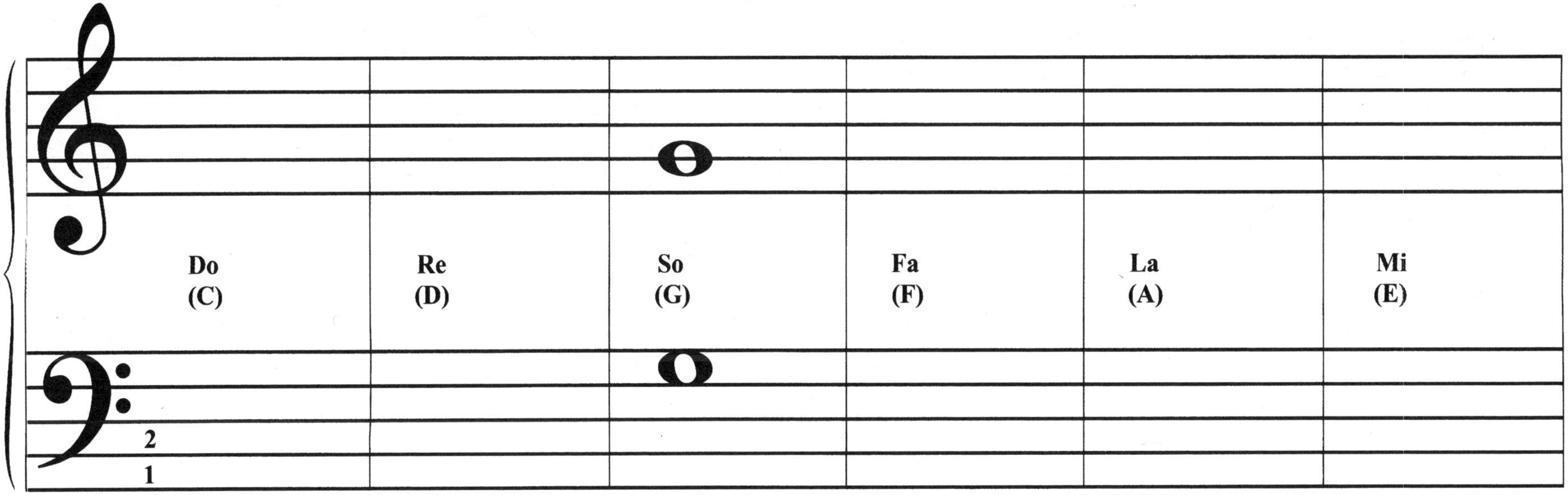

	Do (C)	Mi (E)	Fa (F)	La (A)	So (G)	Ti (B)

	Do (C)	Re (D)	So (G)	Fa (F)	La (A)	Mi (E)

Billy and the Piano

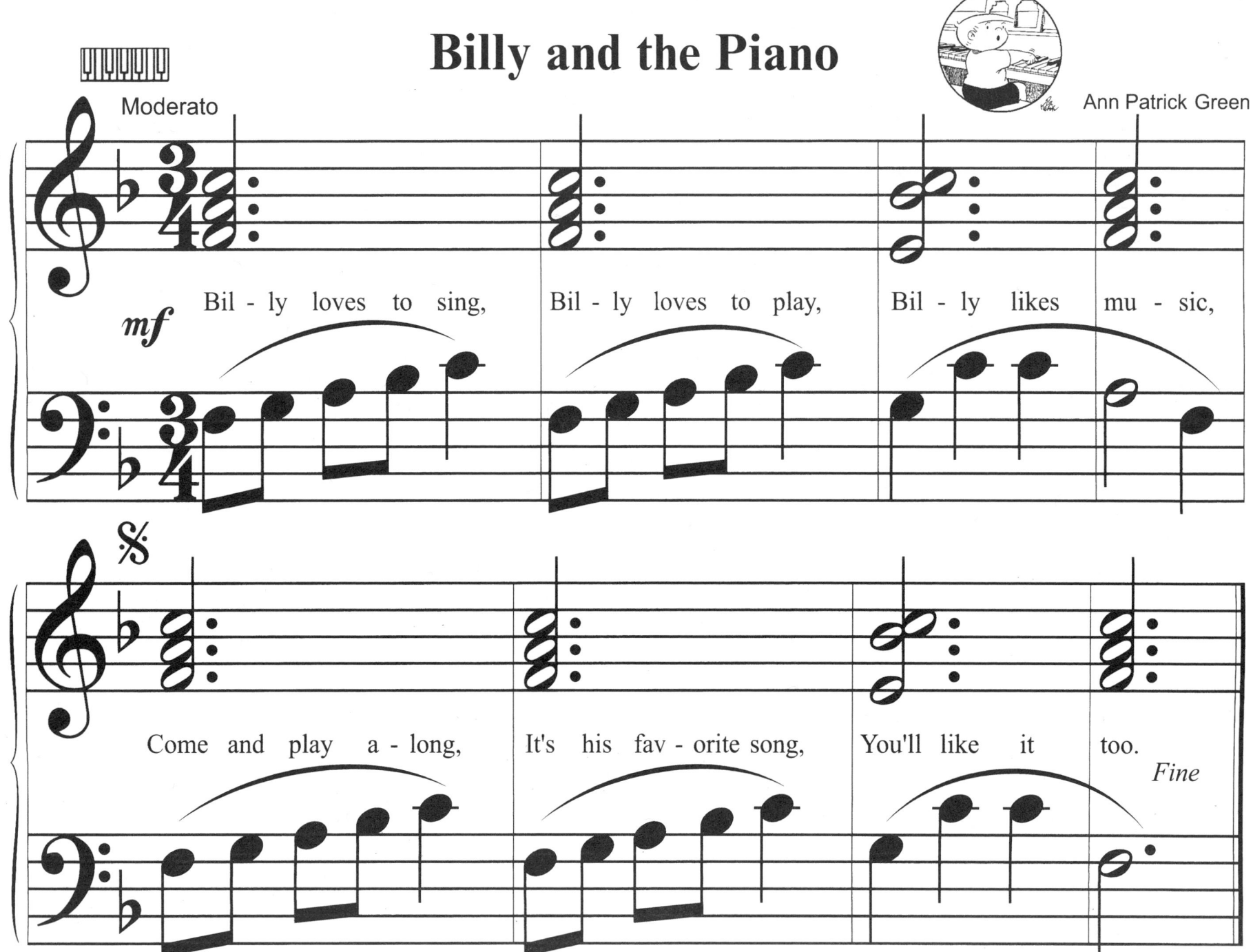

Ann Patrick Green

Moderato

mf

Bil - ly loves to sing, Bil - ly loves to play, Bil - ly likes mu - sic,

Come and play a - long, It's his fav - orite song, You'll like it too. *Fine*

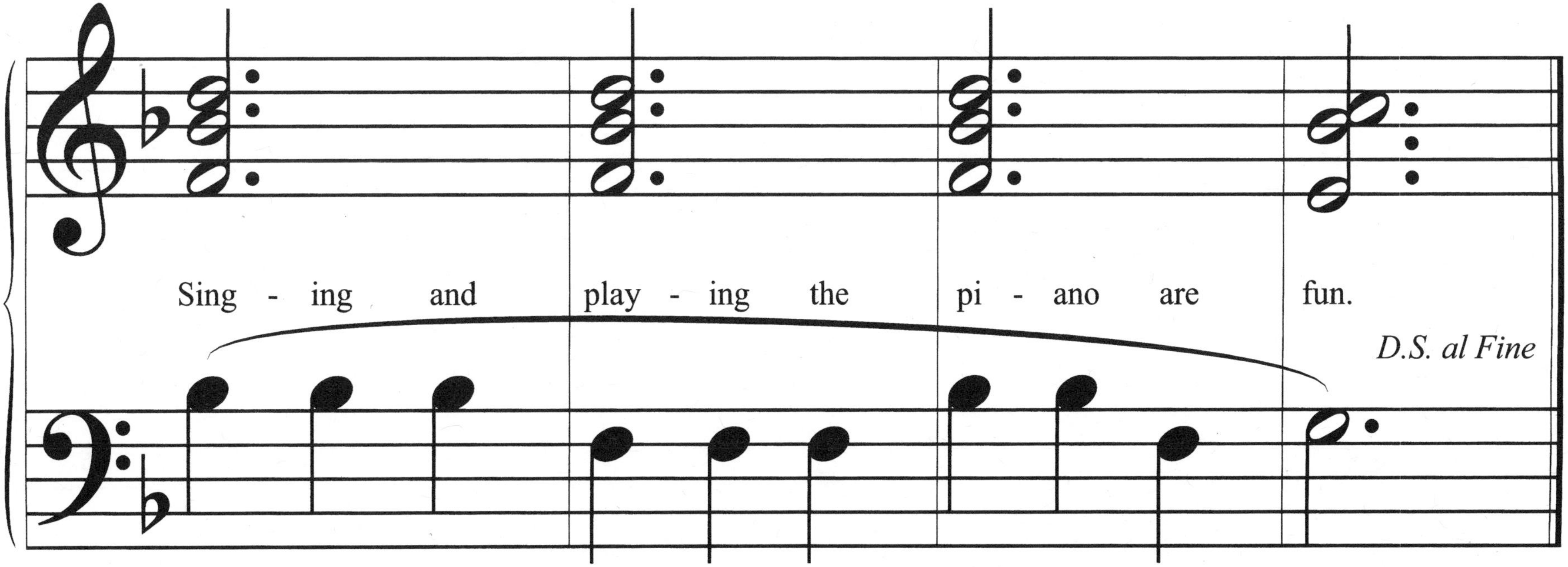

Sing - ing and play - ing the pi - ano are fun.

D.S. al Fine

London Bridge

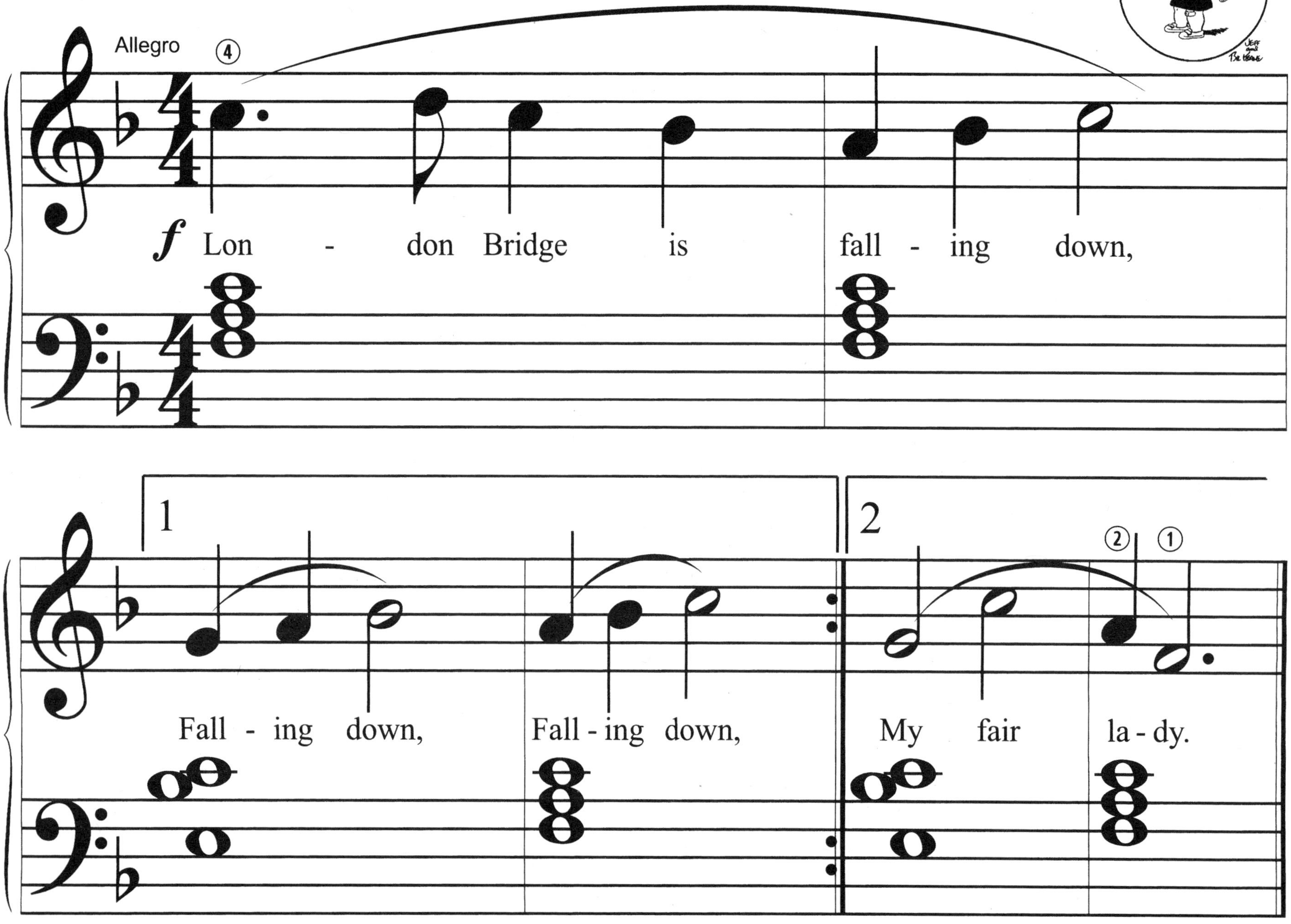

Allegro ④

f Lon - don Bridge is fall - ing down,

1 Fall - ing down, Fall - ing down,

2 My fair la - dy.

Note Identification

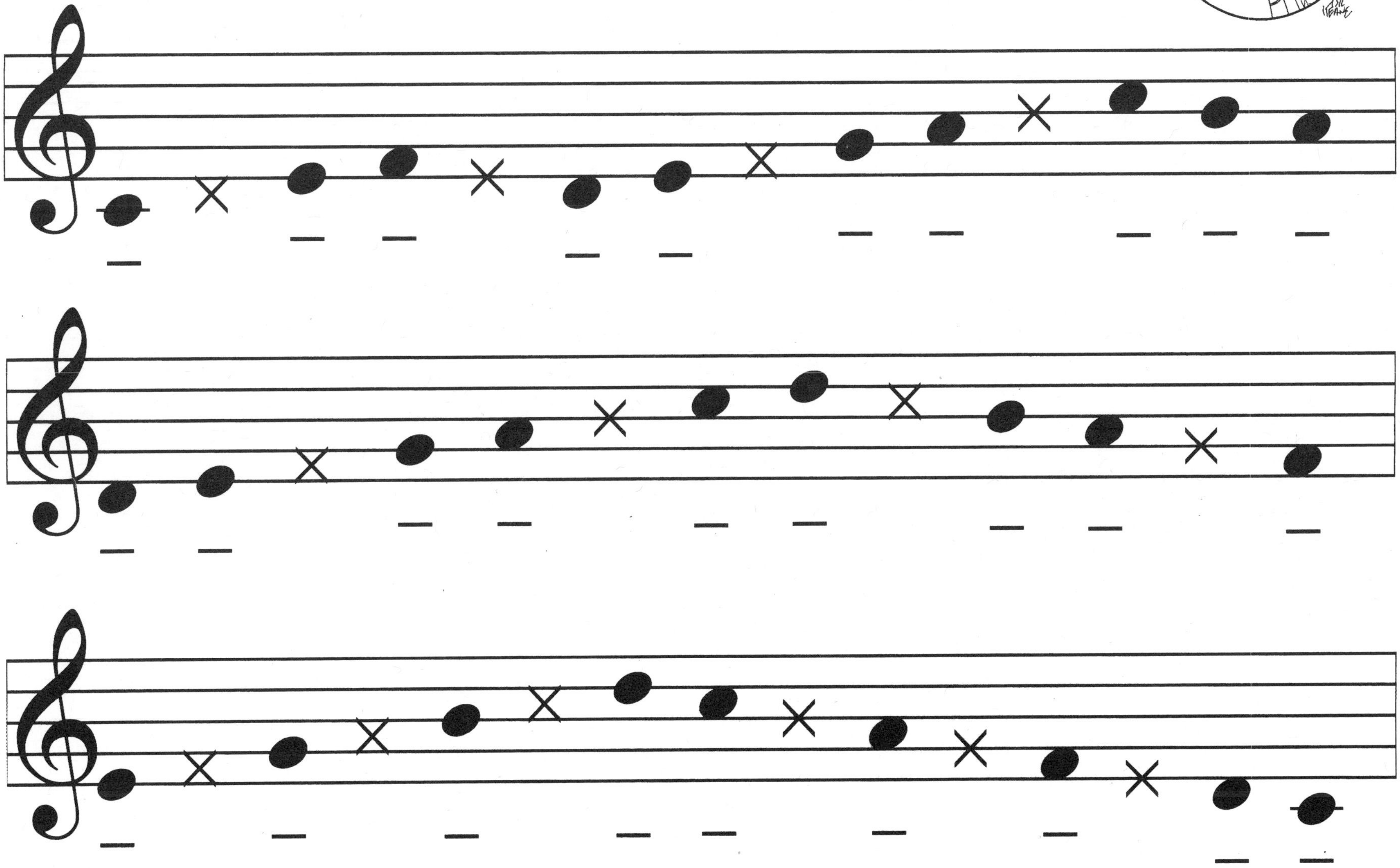

Note Identification

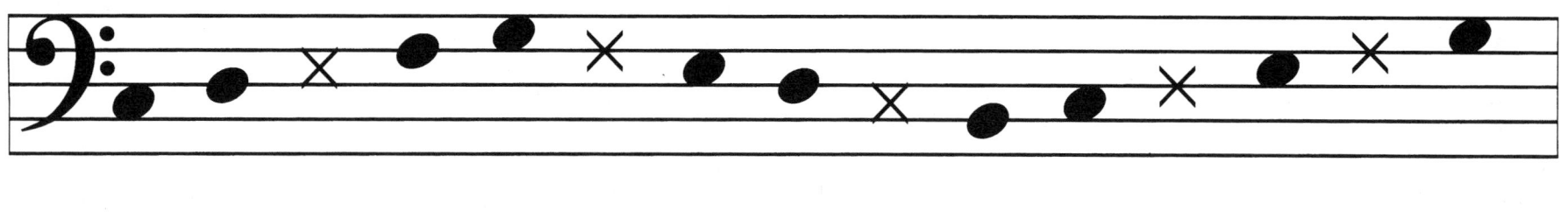

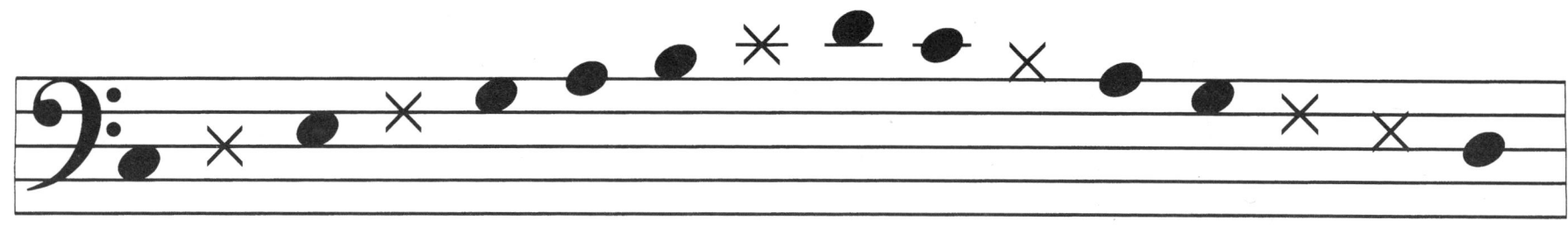

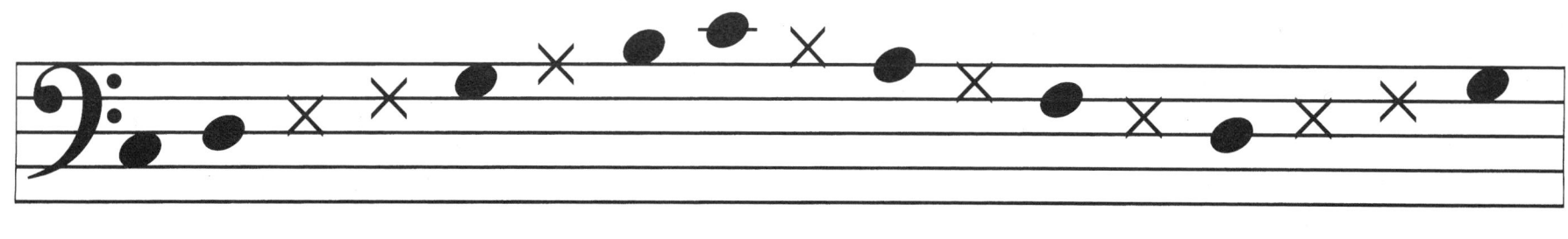

Thanksgiving Day

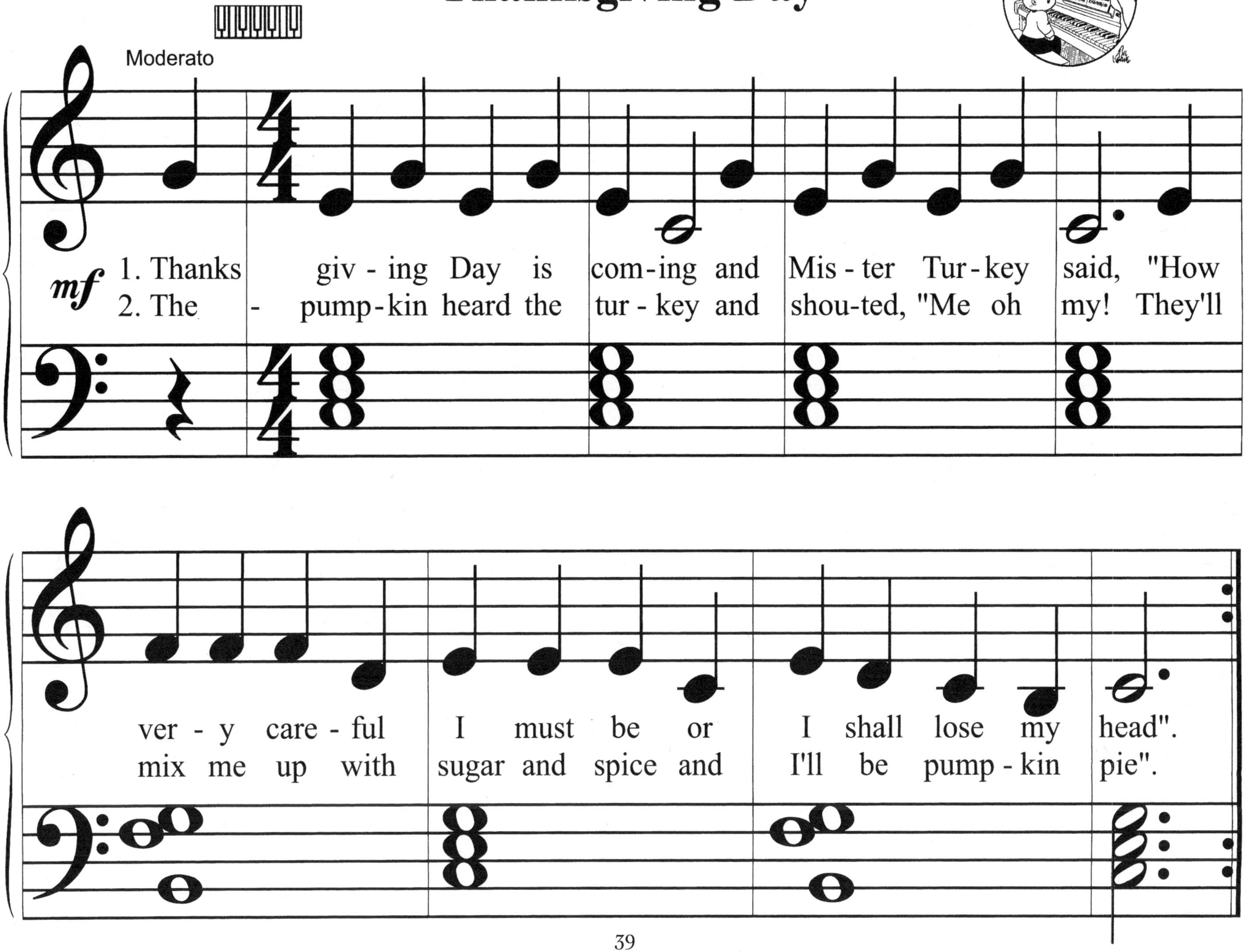

Moderato

mf

1. Thanks- giv - ing Day is com-ing and Mis - ter Tur-key said, "How
2. The pump-kin heard the tur - key and shou-ted, "Me oh my! They'll

ver - y care - ful I must be or I shall lose my head".
mix me up with sugar and spice and I'll be pump - kin pie".

Dreydl

I have a lit-tle Drey-dl, I made it out of clay, And

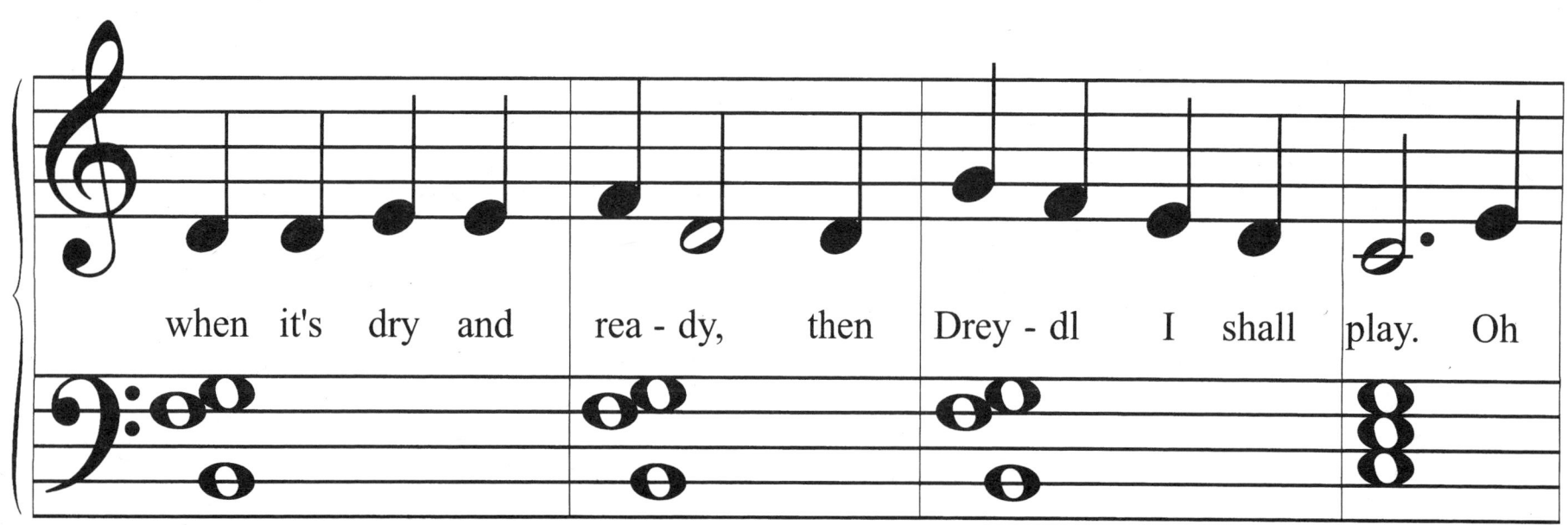

when it's dry and rea-dy, then Drey-dl I shall play. Oh

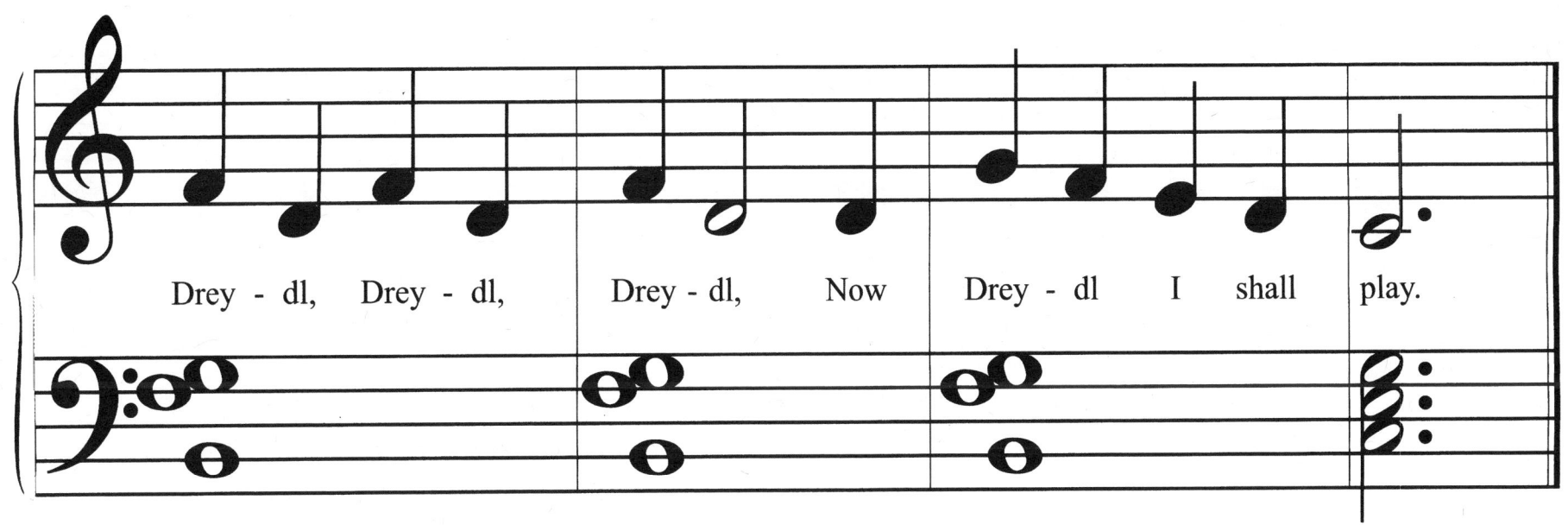

Jingle Bells

Arranged by:
Heather Patrick

Jin - gle Bells, Jin - gle Bells,

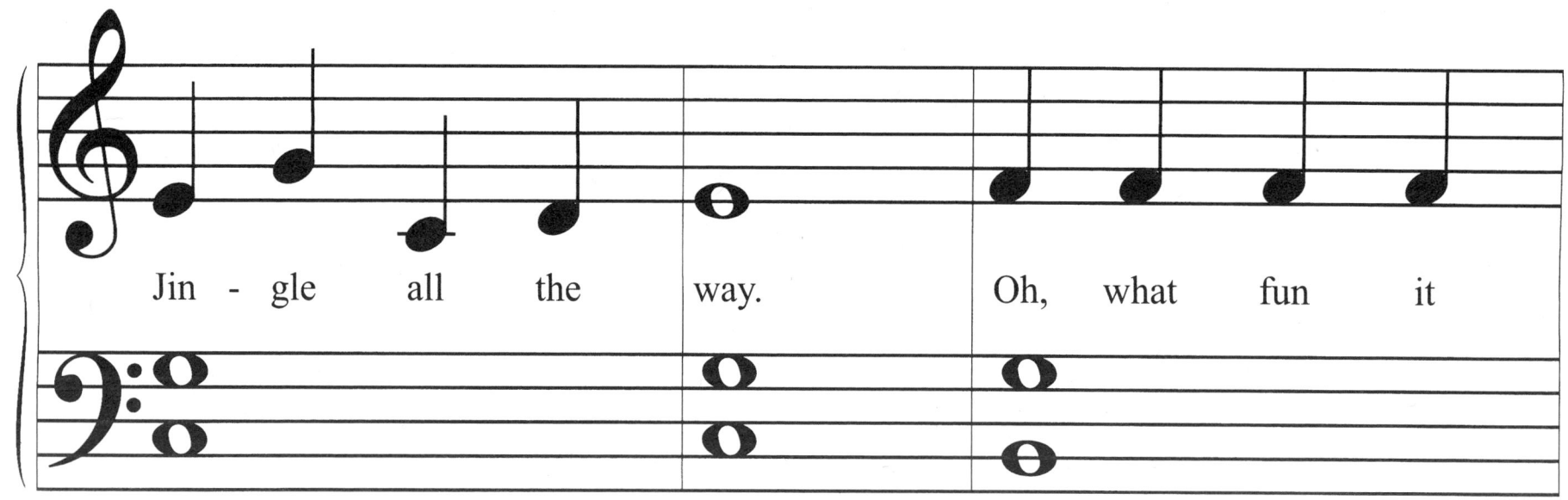

Jin - gle all the way. Oh, what fun it

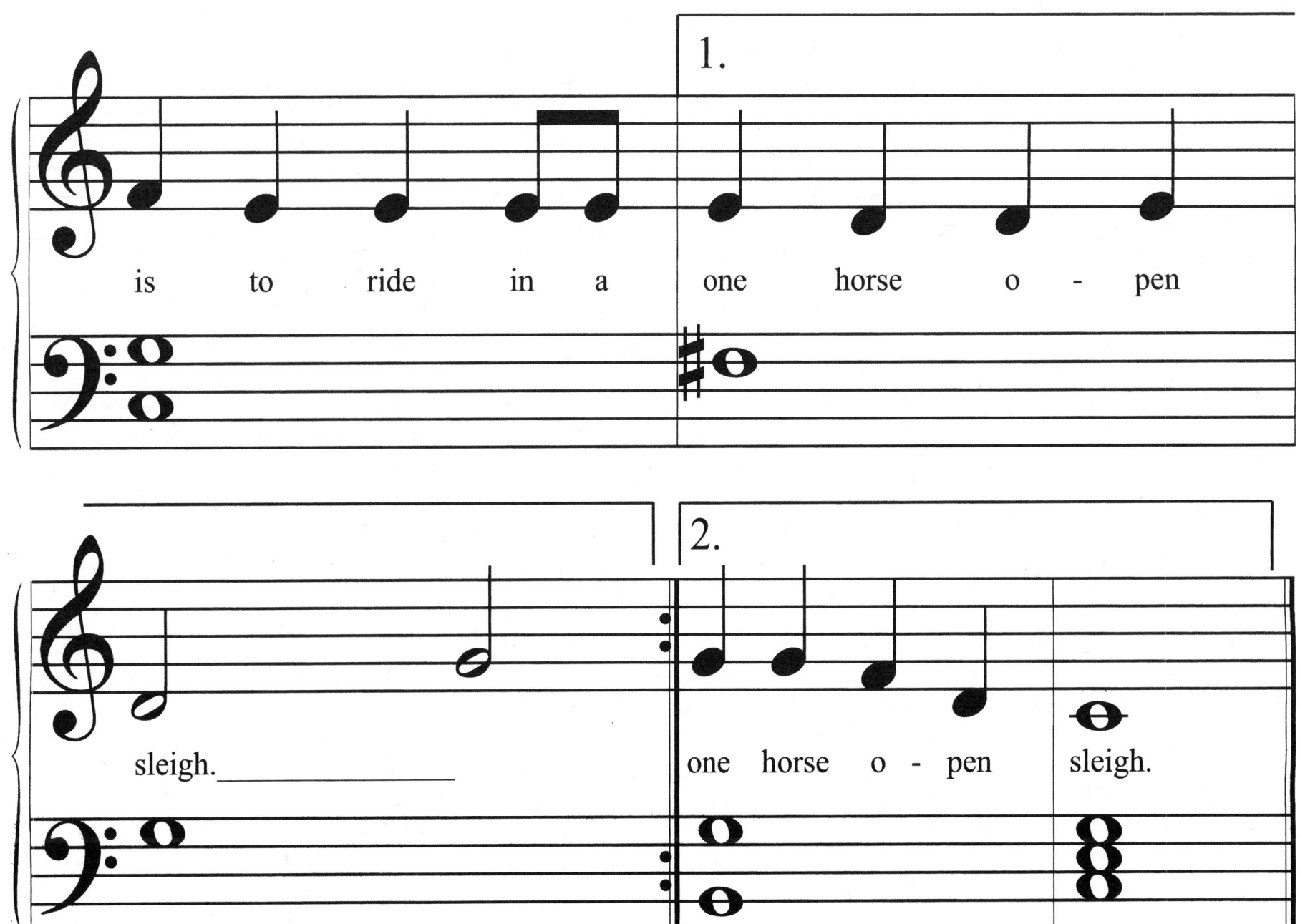

Dictionary of Music

Term	Abbreviation or sign	Meaning
Accent	>	Play the particular note louder where this sign appears
Adagio		Play slowly
Allegretto		Play at a medium fast rate of speed
Allegro		Play at a fast rate of speed
Andante		Play at a medium slow "walking" speed
Crescendo	⟨—⟩	Play gradually louder
Da Capo al Fine	D.C. al Fine	Return to the beginning and play to the word "Fine"
Dal Segno al Fine	D.S. al Fine	Return to the sign (𝄋) and play to the word "Fine"
Diminuendo	Dim. ⟩—⟨	Play gradually softer
Dotted quarter note	♩·	Where a quarter note equals one beat, this note plus the dot equals 1½ beats.
Fermata	⌒	Hold the note longer than it's value
Fine		The end
Flat	♭	Lower the note a half step to the left. It is usually a black key.
Forte	*f*	Play loud
Largo		Play very slowly
Mezzoforte	*mf*	Play medium loud
Mezzopiano	*mp*	Play medium soft
Moderato		Play at medium speed
Piano	*p*	Play softly

Term	Abbreviation or sign	Meaning
Phrase line		Line which divides a piece musically, somewhat like a phrase in literature.
Repeat sign		Repeat section in between the dots or return to the beginning.
Staccato		Release the key quickly, allowing it to come to the surface as soon as sound is heard. The resulting sound will be short and disconnected.
Tie		With notes connected in this way and of the same pitch, do not repeat the second note but hold both for their combined value.
Upbeat		Also called pick-up note or notes which precede the first measure. All counts in an upbeat are subtracted from the last measure of the piece or section.
Vivace		Play with joy, in a lively mood.

Certificate of Accomplishment
Is awarded to:

_____

(Student's Name)

For successfully completing:
Piano Music for Little Fingers Book 2

*On*_____*Teacher*_____

(Date)   (Teacher's Signature)